THE
IRISH
GOLF
ALMANAC

Bill Skinner

Gill & Macmillan

Published in Ireland
by Gill & Macmillan Ltd
Goldenbridge, Dublin 8
with associated companies throughout the world

Created and produced by
Eric Dobby Publishing

© 1995 Eric Dobby Publishing Ltd
© 1995 Text Bill Skinner

A catalogue record is available for this book from the British Library.

ISBN: 0-7171-2295-6

Typeset in Times New Roman by Kevin O'Connor
Printed in Slovenia

Cork Golf Club

Ballycastle Golf Club

CONTENTS

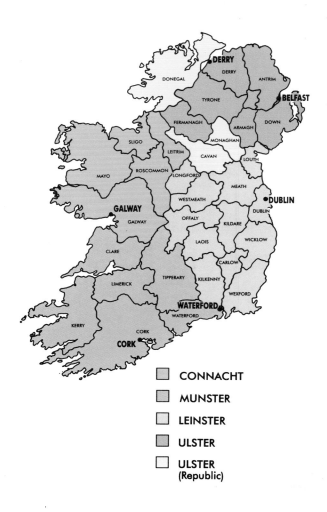

DERRY

DONEGAL

DERRY

ANTRIM

TYRONE

BELFAST

FERMANAGH

ARMAGH

DOWN

SLIGO

MONAGHAN

LEITRIM

CAVAN

LOUTH

MAYO

ROSCOMMON

LONGFORD

MEATH

WESTMEATH

DUBLIN

GALWAY

GALWAY

OFFALY

DUBLIN

KILDARE

CLARE

LAOIS

WICKLOW

CARLOW

LIMERICK

TIPPERARY

KILKENNY

WEXFORD

WATERFORD

KERRY

WATERFORD

CORK

CORK

☐ CONNACHT

☐ MUNSTER

☐ LEINSTER

☐ ULSTER

☐ ULSTER
(Republic)

INTRODUCTION

The Irish Golf Almanac includes a selection of the finest and friendliest golf clubs on the whole island of Ireland. The visiting golf enthusiast is assured of a warm welcome at any of the 200 clubs featured in this book, all of which the author and publishers would like to thank for contributing details and, in some cases, visual material.

The selection has been designed to include both illustrious championship courses and the less well-known club courses - a range of venues to appeal to high and low handicapper alike. The intention has been to achieve as comprehensive a geographical coverage as possible so that, wherever you are staying in Ireland, you will find a golf course within easy reach described in these pages.

To assist the visitor, the book has been arranged in sections according to the four provinces of Ireland (Connacht, Leinster, Munster, Ulster). Within these provinces, in alphabetical order, are the counties, and the courses are arranged alphabetically within those county divisions. It is hoped that this arrangement will be useful to those planning their golfing holidays, the courses described for each county obviously being within easy travelling distance.

In the case of Ulster, there is a further subdivision: Northern Ireland and the Republic, for the province of Ulster contains three counties (Cavan, Donegal, Monaghan) that are part of the Republic. The section for County Down also includes those courses that are in Belfast, even though it is technically a separate administrative area; this is because it would have seemed slightly absurd to have a Belfast section that did not include Royal Belfast Golf Club - which is actually located in County Down. Naturally, there is a final index of course names, so if you want to play a particular course, you will be able to find it swiftly and easily. Locator maps give a general indication of the provinces, the counties and the major cities within them. Many of the entries also include details on how to reach the courses from major roads and motorways.

The main focus has been to describe the courses in terms of their accessibility, features (degree of difficulty) and the facilities they offer. In order to make certain key features obvious at a glance, some information has been provided in the form of highlighted boxes within each entry. Information provided in this form includes the following:

Requirements

H = Handicap certificate required

M = Membership of another club required

Facilities

C = Club hire   T = Trolley hire

Ca = Caddy availability

Pc = Power caddy (motorized trolley) hire

B = Buggy (powered golf cart) hire

Any qualification to these requirements or facilities is included in parenthesis immediately after the relevant icon, and the absence of an icon obviously means that, at the time of writing, the requirement or facility was not in force or available.

The information in the book has come directly from the clubs themselves and is as accurate and up-to-date as possible. However, the publishers cannot accept any liability whatsoever relating to the accuracy or otherwise of the information included.

Figures given for courses' statistics are, by and large, for the competition tee positions and the men's par. Measurements are in metres or yards (occasionally both) as supplied by the club scorecard. Every effort has been made to indicate the times when visitors are restricted from teeing off, but even in cases when the information is highly specific - or even when there appear to be few if any limitations - the advice must always remain that visitors should telephone the club before turning up, in order to avoid disappointment. Please note that the telephone numbers as listed include an initial zero in the prefix. This can be omitted when phoning from outside the Republic of Ireland (International Code +353). When phoning from inside the area where the club is located, the entire prefix may be omitted: just dial the local number.

Phoning ahead and making sure that you meet all the necessary requirements of the club will guarantee you a warm and friendly reception. What can also be guaranteed is that you will be playing golf in some of the most spectacular surroundings available anywhere in the world. Whether it's a lush parkland course or one of the many great links clubs that are perhaps the major feature of golf in Ireland, the choice is yours. Enjoy!

CONNACHT GOLF CLUBS

Co. Galway
Athenry
Ballinasloe
Connemara
Galway
Oughterard

Co. Mayo
Achill
Ashford Castle
Castlebar
Mulrany
Westport

Co. Roscommon
Athlone

Co. Sligo
County Sligo
Enniscrone
Strandhill
Tubbercurry

ATHENRY GOLF CLUB
(ESTABLISHED 1902)
Palmerstown, Oranmore, Co. Galway

The course is located half a mile off the main Galway/Dublin Road, eight miles from Galway and six miles from Athenry. Following his visit in October 1991, Christy O'Connor wrote: "They can be very proud of their new course in Athenry. It is surprisingly dry for an inland course and the greens in particular were magnificent. They may never stage the Ryder Cup in Athenry but, if you are in the area, do yourself a favour and play this eighteen-hole course that adds to the fine venues west of the Shannon." Excellent clubhouse facilities include bar and restaurant and views of the 'Fields of Athenry'.

Secretary:	Eileen Burke Tel 091 44502
Professional:	None
Type:	Parkland
No of holes:	18
Length:	5552 metres
Par:	70
Visitors:	Visitors welcome
Requirements:	None
Handicap Limits:	None
Restrictions:	Tee times not available on Sundays or public holidays. Other times subject to checking - call 091 94466.
Parties:	Contact Luke Glynn, Bally David, Athenry – call 091 44302
Green fees:	IR£12 - IR£15 per round
Hire facilities:	🇹 Ca
Practice ground:	Large practice area and putting green
Catering:	Full catering facilities

BALLINASLOE GOLF CLUB
(ESTABLISHED 1894)

Rossgloss, Ballinasloe, Co. Galway

A rolling parkland course with excellent fairways and greens. Many interesting holes with doglegs right and left and elevated greens. With its newly refurbished clubhouse the course extends to golfers a warm and challenging welcome.

Secretary:	Mary Uniacke Tel 0905 42538
Professional:	None
Type:	Parkland
No of holes:	18
Length:	5868 metres
Par:	72
Visitors:	Visitors welcome
Requirements:	**M**
Handicap Limits:	Juniors only
Restrictions:	Visitors are welcome on weekdays and there is limited availability at weekends. Juniors must have handicap.
Parties:	Please contact Tom Glynn, c/o Ballinasloe Golf Club
Green fees:	IR£10 per round weekdays, IR£12 at weekends and public holidays. IR£5 (IR£6) with member.
Hire facilities:	**T**
Practice ground:	Short practice ground beside clubhouse
Catering:	Catering available throughout the summer and by arrangement during off-peak times

CONNEMARA GOLF CLUB
(ESTABLISHED 1973)
Ballyconneely, Clifden, Co. Galway

In the midst of the natural beauty of Connemara you will find this
championship links. Designed by Eddie Hackett, this is as tough a
challenge as you are likely to find anywhere, with the par of 72 seldom
matched. The back nine have been described as 'the equal of any in the
world'.

Secretary:	John McLaughlin Tel 095 23502/23602
	Fax 095 23662
Professional:	None
Type:	Links
No of holes:	18
Length:	6611 metres
Par:	72
Visitors:	Visitors welcome
Requirements:	H
Handicap Limits:	None
Restrictions:	Visitors welcome at all times
Parties:	Special group discounts available - contact John McLaughlin
Green fees:	IR£18 per round
Hire facilities:	C T Ca B
Practice ground:	Fairway and net, putting and chipping greens
Catering:	Full bar and restaurant facilities. Full *à la carte* menu.

Connemara Golf Club: 10th hole

GALWAY GOLF CLUB
(ESTABLISHED 1895)
Blackrock, Salthill, Co. Galway

Eighteen-hole layout by Galway Bay. Attractive tree-lined course with hillocks, gorse and shrubbery. Features superb views of Galway Bay.

Secretary:	Padraic Fahy Tel 091 22033
Professional:	Don Wallace Tel 091 23038
Type:	Parkland
No of holes:	18
Length:	6370 yards
Par:	71
Visitors:	Visitors welcome
Requirements:	H M
Handicap Limits:	None
Restrictions:	None stated
Parties:	Please contact Secretary
Green fees:	£15 per day
Hire facilities:	C Ca B
Practice ground:	No
Catering:	Full catering facilities available

OUGHTERARD GOLF CLUB
(ESTABLISHED 1973)
Oughterard, Co. Galway

Oughterard Golf Club is situated on N59 adjacent to the 15th-century Aughnanure Castle, 15 miles west of Galway city en route to Connemara. It is a delightful eighteen-hole course, excellently maintained for the discerning golfer. Mature trees demand thought and accuracy from the tee, and elevated greens require precision and patience. The relatively short front nine injects a false sense of security which is quickly deflated on some very testing holes over the inward nine, leaving the player with memories of a fair but demanding course.

Secretary:	John Waters Tel 091 82131 Fax 091 82733
Professional:	Michael Ryan Tel 091 82131/82626
Type:	Mature parkland
No of holes:	18
Length:	6041 yards (5522 metres)
Par:	70
Visitors:	Visitors welcome
Requirements:	H
Handicap Limits:	Gentlemen 28; Ladies 36; Juniors 18
Restrictions:	Gentlemen and Ladies - avoid Ladies Day (Wednesday). Ladies: Monday to Friday, preferably before 4.00pm. Juniors: mornings only Monday to Friday.
Parties:	Contact Secretary
Green fees:	IR£13 per day
Hire facilities:	C T Ca
Practice ground:	Practice area, bunkers and putting green
Catering:	Excellent dining facilities with full *à la carte* menu available daily up to 10.00pm (11.00pm summer time)

Oughterard Golf Club

ACHILL GOLF CLUB
(ESTABLISHED 1952)
Keel, Achill Island, Co. Mayo

This is a nine-hole links course in a scenic setting on the edge of the Atlantic Ocean. The course is more challenging than it looks at first sight and is a place where visitors will find the warmest of welcomes.

Secretary:	Mr P. Lavelle Tel 098 43456
Professional:	None
Type:	Links
No of holes:	9
Length:	2723 yards
Par:	35
Visitors:	Visitors welcome
Requirements:	None
Handicap Limits:	None
Restrictions:	None stated
Parties:	Welcome by arrangement with Secretary
Green fees:	IR£4 for 18 holes
Hire facilities:	C B
Practice ground:	None
Catering:	None

ASHFORD CASTLE GOLF CLUB
(ESTABLISHED 1972)
Cong, Co. Mayo

A nine-hole parkland course with tee positions for gentlemen and ladies.
Ladies length for nine holes 2253 yards. Play round twice from same tees
for eighteen holes. Course run by Ashford Castle Hotel.

Secretary:	Ashford Castle Hotel Tel 092 46003 Fax 092 46260
Professional:	None
Type:	Parkland
No of holes:	9
Length:	2896 yards
Par:	35
Visitors:	Visitors welcome
Requirements:	None
Handicap Limits:	None
Restrictions:	No restrictions
Parties:	Contact duty manager at Ashford Castle Hotel
Green fees:	IR£15 per round or per day
Hire facilities:	[T] [Ca]
Practice ground:	No
Catering:	Thatched cottage tea rooms

Score card details

Hole	1	2	3	4	5	6	7	8	9	10	11	12	13	14	15	16	17	18
Yds	320	340	391	136	384	494	381	289	161	320	340	391	136	384	494	381	289	161
Par	4	4	4	3	4	5	4	4	3	4	4	4	3	4	5	4	4	3

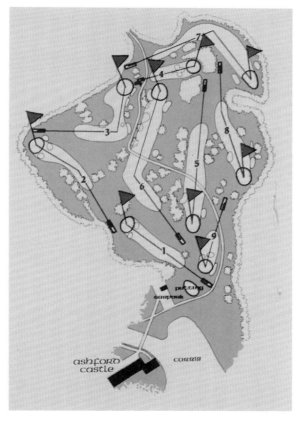

Ashford Castle Golf Club: course plan

CASTLEBAR GOLF CLUB
(ESTABLISHED 1910)
Rocklands, Castlebar, Co. Mayo

A very pleasant eighteen-hole parkland course in an attractive setting.

Secretary:	Angus Ryan Tel 094 32232
Professional:	None
Type:	Parkland
No of holes:	18
Length:	5698 metres
Par:	71
Visitors:	Visitors welcome
Requirements:	[M]
Handicap Limits:	None
Restrictions:	Visitors restricted all day Sunday and on Saturday afternoons
Parties:	Please contact Secretary. Arrangements to be confirmed beforehand.
Green fees:	IR£12 per round weekdays. IR£15 at weekends. Groups of 8+ IR£9 Monday to Friday, IR£11 weekends.
Hire facilities:	[T] [B]
Practice ground:	Small area for short iron practice only
Catering:	Part-time catering service during summer time. Please check beforehand - special arrangements can be made. Snacks and grills available.

MULRANY GOLF CLUB
(ESTABLISHED 1968)
Mulrany, Westport, Co. Mayo

Pleasant nine-hole links course by Clew Bay.

Secretary:	Declan Nevin Tel 098 41568
Professional:	None
Type:	Links
No of holes:	9 (played from outward and inward tees)
Length:	6380 yards
Par:	71
Visitors:	Visitors welcome
Requirements:	M
Handicap Limits:	Gentlemen 24; Ladies 36
Restrictions:	Visitors welcome any time but ring in advance to avoid competition times
Parties:	Contact Secretary, or John Joyce on 098 36185
Green fees:	IR£6 per day. Groups IR£5.
Hire facilities:	C T Ca
Practice ground:	Small putting green
Catering:	Tea and coffee only

WESTPORT GOLF CLUB
(ESTABLISHED 1973)
Carrowholly, Westport, Co. Mayo

Westport is an eighteen-hole championship golf course set in 260 acres of rolling parkland on the shores of Clew Bay and nestling in the shadow of Croagh Patrick, Ireland's famous Holy Mountain. The course was designed by the British firm of golf course architects Hawtree and Sons, and contains many superb holes. Perhaps the best known and most exciting is the par 5 15th (580yds), which features a long carry from the tee over an inlet from Clew Bay. Other great golfing holes are the 9th, 12th and 14th - all par 3s over 180 yards demanding tee shots of accuracy and courage.

Secretary:	Manager James McNamara, Sec. Margaret O'Grady Tel 098 25113/27070 Fax 098 27217
Professional:	Alex Mealia Tel 098 27481
Type:	Parkland
No of holes:	18
Length:	6950 yards
Par:	73
Visitors:	Visitors welcome
Requirements:	H only for competitions
Handicap Limits:	Gentlemen 28; Ladies 36; Juniors 28
Restrictions:	Sundays 7.30 - 11.30am and 12.30 - 5.00pm, Wednesdays and Saturdays 8.00 - 9.30am and 1.00 - 3.00pm
Parties:	Contact Manager or Secretary
Green fees:	IR£18 per round weekdays, IR£22 weekends
Hire facilities:	C T Ca B
Practice ground:	None
Catering:	Full catering and bar facilities

Westport Golf Club

ATHLONE GOLF CLUB

(ESTABLISHED 1892)

Hodson Bay, Athlone, Co. Roscommon

Situated three miles outside Athlone on the shores of Lough Ree, Athlone Golf Club is steadily growing in reputation as recent improvements to the course have made it into a fine test of golf. Trojan efforts by successive committees have finally borne fruit as Athlone has recently been chosen to host the National Cups and Shield Finals in 1998 - a great honour for the club. Visitors are particularly welcome and will no doubt enjoy the course and the friendly ambience of the clubhouse with its excellent facilities.

Secretary:	Dermot Fagan Tel 0902 92073
Professional:	Martin Quinn Tel 0902 92073
Type:	Parkland
No of holes:	18
Length:	6511 yards (5922 metres)
Par:	71
Visitors:	Visitors welcome
Requirements:	H (desirable)
Handicap Limits:	Gentlemen 22; Ladies 28; Juniors 22
Restrictions:	Visitors welcome at all times - booking in advance advisable
Parties:	Contact the office on 0902 92073
Green fees:	IR£12 weekdays, IR£15 weekends. Special rates for parties negotiable.
Hire facilities:	C T Ca B
Practice ground:	Practice ground. Driving range close by.
Catering:	Full bar and catering facilities

COUNTY SLIGO GOLF CLUB

(ESTABLISHED 1894)

Rosses Point, Co. Sligo

Described by Peter Alliss as "... a tremendous test for the highest quality player and great fun for the modest competitor", the club has hosted most of Ireland's major championships in its long and venerable history. Three large beaches beneath the cliffs keep the Atlantic at bay to the west of the course, while towering Benbulben competes with the ocean for scenic splendour on the land side. The wind from the sea is a constant factor but the 3rd, 5th, 10th and 14th holes have very satisfying downhill drives to compensate. Venue of Home Internationals, 1991.

Secretary:	Noel Keyes, Hon. Sec. Tel 071 77186
	Fax 071 77460
Professional:	Leslie Robinson Tel 071 77171
Type:	Links
No of holes:	18
Length:	6565 yards (6003 metres)
Par:	71
Visitors:	Visitors welcome
Requirements:	H may be requested; M
Handicap Limits:	Gentlemen 28; Ladies 36; Juniors 18
Restrictions:	All visitors restricted Saturdays, Sundays and public holidays. Also Ladies Day - Tuesday.
Parties:	For groups of 12 or more green fees IR£13 per person midweek and IR£20 weekends.
Green fees:	Monday to Friday IR£16 per round, IR£22 Saturday, Sunday and public holidays. IR£27 per day Monday to Friday.
Hire facilities:	C T Ca B
Practice ground:	Putting and chipping area
Catering:	Dining room and bar available

Co. Sligo Golf Club

ENNISCRONE GOLF CLUB

(ESTABLISHED 1918)

Enniscrone, Co. Sligo

"Enniscrone is a particularly beautiful links on the bay of Killala ... a course with some amazing holes" (Peter Dobereiner). "Nature decreed that Enniscrone should have a superb links and it has worked out that way. Anybody matching the par of 72 will have performed very creditably indeed" (Charles Mulqueen - *Ireland's Top Golf Courses*). Located 13km from Ballina Town, 56km from Horan International Airport (Knock) and 55km from Sligo Regional Airport.

Secretary:	John Fleming Tel 096 36297 Fax 096 36657
Professional:	Charles McGolderick Tel 096 36297
	Home 096 71021
Type:	Links
No of holes:	18
Length:	6720 yards
Par:	72
Visitors:	Visitors welcome
Requirements:	None
Handicap Limits:	None
Restrictions:	Gentlemen: Saturday 8.00 - 9.30am, 1.30 - 3.00pm and Sunday 7.00 - 10.30am, 1.30 - 3.00pm. Ladies: Sundays 12.30 - 1.30pm and 3.00 - 4.00pm.
Parties:	Contact Mrs. Anne Freeman (Administrator) 096 36297
Green fees:	Range from IR£10-IR£18 per round depending on weekday/weekend and high/low season
Hire facilities:	[C] [T] [Ca] [Pc] [B]
Practice ground:	Extensive practice area and putting green
Catering:	Full bar and catering. Please order prior to play.

Enniscrone Golf Club

STRANDHILL GOLF CLUB
(ESTABLISHED 1931)
Strandhill, Co. Sligo

Popular links course - very good quality.

Secretary:	Jim Mungovan Tel 071 68438/68188
Professional:	None
Type:	Links
No of holes:	18
Length:	6032 yards (5516 metres)
Par:	69
Visitors:	Visitors welcome
Requirements:	M
Handicap Limits:	Gentlemen 28; Ladies 36; Juniors 20
Restrictions:	All visitors restricted on Saturday and Sunday up to 11.00am and 1.00 - 3.00pm
Parties:	Please contact Secretary
Green fees:	IR£14 per round. Society rate IR£12.
Hire facilities:	T Ca
Practice ground:	Practice ground available
Catering:	Catering available

TUBBERCURRY GOLF CLUB
(ESTABLISHED 1991)
Ballymote Road, Tubbercurry, Co. Sligo

Old club on new parkland site.

Secretary:	Joe Kilcoyne Tel 071 85216
Professional:	None
Type:	Parkland
No of holes:	9
Length:	5490 metres
Par:	70
Visitors:	Visitors welcome
Requirements:	None
Handicap Limits:	None
Restrictions:	None
Parties:	Contact Secretary
Green fees:	IR£6 per round or per day
Hire facilities:	None
Practice ground:	Putting green and chipping area
Catering:	None as yet. New clubhouse is being built.

LEINSTER GOLF CLUBS

Co. Carlow
Carlow

Co. Dublin
Balbriggan
Balcarrick
Beaverstown
Beech Park
Castle
Clontarf
Deer Park
Dun Laoghaire
Edmondstown
Elm Park
Forrest Little
Grange
Hazel Grove
Hermitage
Hollystown
Howth
The Island
Killiney
Kilternan
Lucan
Luttrellstown
  Castle
Malahide
Milltown
Newlands
Portmarnock
Royal Dublin

St. Anne's
Skerries
Slade Valley
Stackstown
Sutton

Co. Kildare
Bodenstown
Castlewarden
The Curragh
Killeen
Kildare
Knockanally

Co. Kilkenny
Kilkenny
Mount Juliet

Co. Laois
Heath (Portlaoise)
Portarlington

Co. Longford
Co. Longford

Co. Louth
Ardee

County Louth
Dundalk
Greenore
Seapoint
Headfort

Co. Meath
Laytown &
  Bettystown
Royal Tara
Trim

Co. Offaly
Birr
Tullamore

Co. Westmeath
Mullingar

Co. Wexford
Courtown

Enniscorthy
Rosslare
Wexford

Co. Wicklow
Arklow
Blainroe
Bray
Charlesland
Delgany
The European
Greystones
Kilcoole
Old Conna
Rathsallagh
Wicklow
Woodbrook
Woodenbridge

CARLOW GOLF CLUB
(ESTABLISHED 1899)
Deerpark, Co. Carlow

Carlow Golf Club is a parkland course laid out in a wild deer park over undulating terrain, with numerous elevated tees, several excellent doglegs and large, slick putting surfaces. There are many long par 4s and the 18th is the most spectacular finishing hole in Ireland. Sandy subsoil makes Carlow playable twelve months of the year and the course is invariably in good condition. Its qualities are further enhanced by the water hazards at the 2nd, 10th and 11th. A relatively short course, there are only two par 5s - one of which is the 18th.

Secretary:	Margaret Meaney Tel 0503 31695
Professional:	Andy Gilbert Tel 0503 41745
Type:	Parkland
No of holes:	18
Length:	6428 yards (5844 metres)
Par:	70
Visitors:	Visitors welcome
Requirements:	M
Handicap Limits:	None
Restrictions:	None stated
Parties:	Contact Secretary - advance booking required
Green fees:	Weekday IR£20 (groups 12+ IR£18) per day
	Weekend IR£25 (groups 12+ IR£22) per day
Hire facilities:	C C (summer) T B
Catering:	Full restaurant open daily 11.00am – 10.00pm

BALBRIGGAN GOLF CLUB
(ESTABLISHED 1945)
Blackhall, Balbriggan, Co. Dublin

The course is located a quarter of a mile south of Balbriggan on the main Belfast/Dublin road. Parkland course with fine views of the Cooley Peninsula and the Mourne Mountains.

Secretary:	Michael O'Halloran, Secretary/Manager
	Tel 01 8412229
Professional:	None
Type:	Parkland
No of holes:	18
Length:	5881 metres
Par:	71
Visitors:	Visitors welcome
Requirements:	None
Handicap Limits:	None
Restrictions:	None - tee times by arrangement preferably. Ladies Day is Tuesday.
Parties:	Please contact Secretary/Manager. Parties welcome by arrangement.
Green fees:	IR£14 per round weekdays. Special rates by arrangement.
Hire facilities:	**B**
Practice ground:	Practice fairway available
Catering:	Full catering available

BALCARRICK GOLF CLUB
(ESTABLISHED 1972/1992)
Corballis, Donabate, Co. Dublin

Originally established in 1972 as Dublin & County Golf Club, Balcarrick Golf Club has a course which is a mixture of links and parkland. Water is featured prominently, with four lakes on the course.

Secretary:	James King Tel 01 8436957
Professional:	None
Type:	Links/parkland
No of holes:	18
Length:	6912 yards
Par:	72
Visitors:	Visitors welcome
Requirements:	None
Handicap Limits:	None
Restrictions:	Juniors restricted on Saturday and Sunday mornings.
Parties:	Please contact James Gubbins
Green fees:	IR£10 weekdays and IR£15 Saturday and Sunday
Hire facilities:	None
Practice ground:	None
Catering:	Teas, coffee and sandwiches Monday, Tuesday, Wednesday and Friday. Grills and snacks Thursday, Saturday and Sunday.

BEAVERSTOWN GOLF CLUB
(ESTABLISHED 1985)

Beaverstown, Donabate, Co. Dublin

A testing parkland course set in a former fruit farm incorporating 46 acres of apple orchards.

Secretary:	Eddie Smyth Tel 01 8436439
Professional:	None
Type:	Parkland
No of holes:	18
Length:	5551 metres
Par:	71
Visitors:	Visitors welcome
Requirements:	None
Handicap Limits:	Gentlemen 28; Ladies 36; Juniors 28
Restrictions:	All visitors restricted on Wednesdays, Saturdays and Sundays. Tee times Monday, Tuesday, Thursday and Friday.
Parties:	Contact Eddie Smyth
Green fees:	IR£12 per round
Hire facilities:	**B**
Practice ground:	Short practice ground available
Catering:	Full bar and catering facilities 10.30am to 11.00pm

BEECH PARK GOLF CLUB
(ESTABLISHED 1973)
Johnstown, Rathcoole, Co. Dublin

Newish course in mature setting and excellent condition.

Secretary:	Joe Deally, Secretary/Manager Tel 01 4580100
Professional:	None
Type:	Parkland
No of holes:	18
Length:	5730 metres
Par:	72
Visitors:	Visitors welcome
Requirements:	None
Handicap Limits:	None
Restrictions:	All visitors restricted Saturday and Sunday
Parties:	Please contact Joe Deally, Secretary/Manager
Green fees:	IR£17 per round. No special rates.
Hire facilities:	🅃 🅱
Practice ground:	Practice ground available
Catering:	Full catering, seven days

CASTLE GOLF CLUB

(ESTABLISHED 1913)

Woodside Drive, Rathfarnham, Dublin 14

Castle is a fine tree-lined parkland course situated four miles from Dublin city centre. It constitutes a very fair test for the high and low handicap golfer. Many amateur and professional events have been staged at this venue.

Secretary:	L. Blackburne, Secretary/Manager
	Tel 01 4904207
Professional:	D. Kinsella Tel 01 4920272
Type:	Parkland
No of holes:	18
Length:	5653 metres
Par:	70
Visitors:	Visitors welcome
Requirements:	None
Handicap Limits:	None
Restrictions:	All visitors restricted at weekends
Parties:	Contact Secretary/Manager
Green fees:	IR£25 per round
Hire facilities:	🇹
Practice ground:	Small practice ground and practice putting
Catering:	Full *à la carte* menu and snack menu

CLONTARF GOLF CLUB
(ESTABLISHED 1911)
Donnycarney House, Malahide Road, Dublin 3

Clontarf is the nearest golf club to Dublin city being only 2½ miles from the city centre. It is a pleasant parkland course with undulating fairways and a liberal sprinkling of fine trees. The feature hole is the 12th (SI 1) with a raised plateau halfway along the fairway followed by a valley with two lakes, then the green - also on a raised plateau. The clubhouse was originally built in 1781 and recently refurbished at a cost of IR£1.25 million; it is a fine example of how the old and the new can be blended together in a splendid architectural edifice.

Secretary:	Mr D. Gilroy Tel 01 8331892 Fax 01 8331933
Professional:	Mr J. Craddock Tel 01 8331877
Type:	Parkland
No of holes:	18
Length:	5459 metres
Par:	69
Visitors:	Visitors welcome
Requirements:	None
Handicap Limits:	None
Restrictions:	Visitors may play as follows, subject to availability of course: Gentlemen Tuesday to Sunday; Ladies Monday and Tuesday and other specified times (please phone); Juniors mornings Monday to Friday.
Parties:	Contact Secretary (8331892). (Dress code applies - no jeans, tracksuits or joggers/sneakers.)
Green fees:	IR£21 per round. No daily rates. Special rates for large groups. Caddies by arrangement.
Hire facilities:	C T Ca
Practice ground:	Practice area for short irons and for putting
Catering:	Dining room plus bar food

DEER PARK HOTEL AND GOLF COURSES
(ESTABLISHED 1973)
Deer Park Hotel and Golf Courses, Howth, Co. Dublin

16 km from Dublin city and 10 km from the airport. Situated on a hillside overlooking Dublin Bay with an uninterrupted view of the coastline, described by H. G. Wells as "the finest view west of Naples". It features the largest golf complex in Ireland and many of the bedrooms have sea views.

Secretary:	David Tighe, Secretary/Manager
	Tel 01 8322624 Fax 01 8392405
Professional:	None

	Course 1: St Fintan's	**Course 2:** Deer Park
Type:	Parkland	Parkland
No of holes:	18	18
Length:	6503 yds (5921 m)	6778 yds (6195 m)
Par:	72	72

Visitors:	Visitors welcome
Requirements:	None
Handicap Limits:	None
Restrictions:	No restrictions for visitors
Parties:	Welcome any time - prior arrangement necessary. Saturday and Sunday bookings require meal bookings in restaurant.
Green fees:	IR£10.50 per round
Hire facilities:	**C** **T**
Practice ground:	Putting green available
Catering:	Deer Park Hotel has 50 en-suite bedrooms, coffee shop, bar and restaurant. Fully inclusive golf holiday rates available.

DUN LAOGHAIRE GOLF CLUB
(ESTABLISHED 1910)
Eglinton Park, Tivoli Road, Dun Laoghaire, Co. Dublin

FOUNDED 1910

The club was founded in 1910 and the course redesigned in 1919 to a revised design by Harry Colt - largely the same design exists today. A parkland course situated 7 miles from Dublin and ¾ mile from Dun Laoghaire Ferry Port. Although the course is not long, many holes require careful club selection.

Secretary:	Mr T. Stewart (Manager) Tel 01 2803916
	Fax 01 2804868
Professional:	Owen Mulhall Tel 01 2801694
Type:	Parkland
No of holes:	18
Length:	5712 yards (5272 metres)
Par:	69
Visitors:	Visitors welcome - except Saturdays
Requirements:	None
Handicap Limits:	None
Restrictions:	None for visiting ladies. Juniors with members only.
Parties:	Contact Club Manager for advance booking. Societies book in advance for Tuesday and Fridays only.
Green fees:	IR£25 per round or per day
Hire facilities:	Arrange with Professional
Practice ground:	Short game only
Catering:	Full restaurant available every day during golf season (April to October)

EDMONDSTOWN GOLF CLUB
(ESTABLISHED 1944)

Edmondstown Road, Edmondstown, Dublin 16

Picturesque parkland course, situated in the foothills of the Dublin Mountains. The 4th (par 5) and the 6th (par 4) require a challenging second or third shot over a scenic meandering stream. The 12th and 13th command beautiful views of the surrounding hills and the long par 4 18th will complete a testing and enjoyable round. Some caddies, caddy cars and power caddies are available, and snooker is available in the clubhouse.

Secretary:	Selwyn S. Davies	
	Tel 01 493 1082 Fax 01 493 3152	
Professional:	Andrew Crofton Tel 01 494 1049	
	Course 1: White	**Course 2:** Yellow/Green
Type:	Parkland	Parkland
No of holes:	18	18
Length:	5663 metres	5393 metres
Par:	70	70

Visitors:	Visitors welcome but advised to phone
Requirements:	None
Handicap Limits:	Gentlemen 28; Ladies 36; Juniors 28
Restrictions:	Societies welcome on Monday, Thursday, Friday and Saturday mornings up to 11.30am
Parties:	Must be booked in advance through Secretary's Office
Tee times:	See above
Green fees:	Weekdays IR£25 per round. Saturday, Sunday and public holidays IR£25. Special rates for societies.
Hire facilities:	C T Ca Pc B
Practice ground:	Practice green and practice field.
Catering:	Full bar/catering facilities all day within the Clubs Registration Laws

ELM PARK GOLF CLUB
(ESTABLISHED 1925)
Nutley House, Nutley Lane, Donnybrook, Dublin 4

Pleasant eighteen holes in mature parkland setting, featuring a stream.

Secretary:	Adrian McCormack, Secretary/Manager
	Tel 01 2693438
Professional:	Seamus Green Tel 01 2692650
Type:	Parkland
No of holes:	18
Length:	5422 metres
Par:	68
Visitors:	Visitors welcome
Requirements:	H M
Handicap Limits:	None
Restrictions:	All visitors contact the Professional
Parties:	Contact the Secretary/Manager
Green fees:	IR£30 per round
Hire facilities:	C B
Practice ground:	None
Catering:	Lunch 12.30 – 2.00pm. Dinner 6.00 – 9.00pm

FORREST LITTLE GOLF CLUB
Cloghran, Co. Dublin

The course is located beside Dublin Airport and is one of the pre-qualifying courses for the Irish Open. A mature tree-lined parkland course featuring a stream which comes into play on several fairways. Many interesting holes. The club hosts an Open Week in June.

Secretary:	Mr A. J. Greany, Secretary/Manager Tel 01 8401183
Professional:	Tony Judd Tel 8407670
Type:	Parkland
No of holes:	18
Length:	5865 metres
Par:	70
Visitors:	Visitors welcome
Requirements:	H M
Handicap Limits:	None
Restrictions:	Visitors are welcome Monday to Friday but avoid Wednesday and Friday afternoons and all weekends.
Parties:	Please contact Secretary/Manager
Green fees:	Green fees not stated but always telephone for appointment
Hire facilities:	C B Pc
Practice ground:	Large practice area
Catering:	Clubhouse open daily 8.00am to midnight

GRANGE GOLF CLUB
(ESTABLISHED 1910)
Whitechurch Road, Rathfarnham, Dublin 16

Six miles from the city centre and picturesquely situated near the Dublin Mountains. The course starts with two par 3s, the first being the longer and more difficult. In all the holes (particularly the 4th and 18th) accuracy off the tees is essential.

Secretary:	James A. O'Donaghue, Secretary/Manager
	Tel 01 493 2889 Fax 01 493 9490
Professional:	Barry Hamill Tel 493 2299 Fax as above
Type:	Parkland
No of holes:	18
Length:	5517 metres
Par:	68
Visitors:	Visitors welcome
Requirements:	Ⓜ
Handicap Limits:	None
Restrictions:	All tee times by prior appointment
Parties:	Contact the Secretary/Manager
Green fees:	IR£28 per round
Hire facilities:	Ⓣ Ⓒa
Practice ground:	Practice ground available
Catering:	Catering facilities available

HAZEL GROVE GOLF CLUB
(ESTABLISHED 1988)
Mount Seskin Road, Tallaght, Dublin 24

Hazel Grove is a nine-hole course offering alternative shots on each round with eleven greens in play and no duplication of tee boxes. Situated eight miles from the city centre, one mile from the Square shopping complex.

Secretary:	Jim Whelan Tel 01 4520911
Professional:	None
Type:	Parkland
No of holes:	9 (played from outward and inward tees)
Length:	5225 yards
Par:	68
Visitors:	Visitors welcome
Requirements:	None
Handicap Limits:	None
Restrictions:	Gentlemen restricted Tuesday and Thursday after 2.00pm, Saturday after 12 noon, no Sundays. Ladies and Juniors restricted Tuesday and Thursday after 2.00pm; no Saturdays or Sundays.
Parties:	Please contact Jim Whelan. Bookings available Monday, Wednesday and Friday and Saturday morning.
Green fees:	IR£7 weekdays, IR£10 Saturday. Special rates by arrangement.
Hire facilities:	🅃
Practice ground:	Practice area and putting green
Catering:	Snacks available. Groups by arrangement.

HERMITAGE GOLF CLUB
(ESTABLISHED 1905)
Lucan, Co. Dublin

Situated in the midst of pleasantly wooded lands that slope gently towards
a four-mile river valley of great charm, the Hermitage course is the least
artificial of the golf courses around Dublin, but it is only a twenty-minute
drive from the city. A new clubhouse was built in 1969, which has been
compared with the Eldorado Club in Palm Springs - a 'Millionaire's
Paradise'. The club has hosted many major competitions in which such
notable stars as Doug Sanders, Severiano Ballesteros, Bob Charles and
Christy O'Connor Jnr have been impressed by the quality of the course.

Secretary:	Tom Spelman, General Manager Tel 01 6268491
Professional:	Ciaran Carroll Tel 01 6268072
Type:	Parkland
No of holes:	18
Length:	5814 metres
Par:	71
Visitors:	Visitors welcome
Requirements:	H M
Handicap Limits:	Gentlemen 24; Ladies 36
Restrictions:	Bookings by phone prior to visit to club to check tee time availability
Parties:	Contact Tom Spelman (General Manager) or Kay Russell (Club Secretary)
Green fees:	1994 prices IR£25 per round. Daily rates on request.
Hire facilities:	C T
Practice ground:	No
Catering:	Full restaurant 12.30 - 9.30pm. Snacks available 10.00am - 9.30pm.

Hermitage Golf Club

Score card details

Holes	1	2	3	4	5	6	7	8	9	10	11	12	13	14	15	16	17	18
Yds	173	400	330	155	305	285	199	380	457	146	492	374	172	320	430	362	366	370
Par	4	4	4	3	5	4	3	4	5	3	5	4	3	4	5	4	4	4

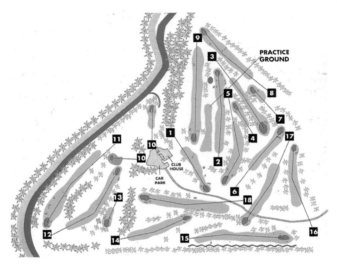

Hermitage Golf Club: course plan

HOLLYSTOWN GOLF CLUB
(ESTABLISHED 1992)
Hollystown, Hollywood Rath, Dublin 15

Well maintained eighteen-hole public course.

Secretary:	Oliver Barry Tel 01 8207444 Fax 01 8207447
Professional:	Adam Whiston, Consultant Tel 01 4626009
Type:	Parkland
No of holes:	18
Length:	5674 metres
Par:	72
Visitors:	Visitors welcome
Requirements:	None
Handicap Limits:	None
Restrictions:	Tee times available seven days a week
Parties:	Please contact Oliver Barry
Green fees:	IR£10 midweek, IR£15 weekends

Hire facilities: 🅲 🆃 🅱

Practice ground: Practice area and putting green
Catering: Coffee shop

HOWTH GOLF CLUB

(ESTABLISHED 1916)

St. Fintan's, Carrickbrack Road, Sutton, Dublin 13

Heathland course, scenic, with pleasant views over Dublin Bay.

Secretary:	Ann MacNiece Tel 01 8323055/8321793
	Fax 01 8321793
Professional:	John McGuirk Tel 01 8393895
Type:	Heathland
No of holes:	18
Length:	5618 metres
Par:	71
Visitors:	Visitors welcome
Requirements:	None
Handicap Limits:	Gentlemen 28; Ladies 36; Juniors 36
Restrictions:	Wednesdays (Ladies Day)
Parties:	Contact Secretary
Green fees:	IR£16 per day Monday, Tuesday, Thursday; IR£18 per day Friday
Hire facilities:	
Practice ground:	Practice ground available
Catering:	Bar catering available - usual bar hours

THE ISLAND GOLF CLUB
(ESTABLISHED 1890)
Corballis, Donabate, Co. Dublin

The Island golf links is located on Corballis Peninsula, two miles east of Donabate. It is an old traditional links although there have been many changes in the design over the years. The present course layout has been the format since 1990, the changes being designed by Fred Hawtree and Eddie Hackett. The club hosted the 1990 Irish Ladies Championship and will host the 1998 Irish Amateur Close Championship.

Secretary:	Liam O'Connor, Secretary/Manager Tel 01 8436462 Fax 01 8436860
Professional:	None
Type:	Links
No of holes:	18
Length:	6053 metres
Par:	71
Visitors:	Visitors welcome
Requirements:	None
Handicap Limits:	None
Restrictions:	Visitors to apply to Secretary. Applications dealt with on ad hoc basis.
Parties:	Please contact the Secretary
Green fees:	IR£27 per round midweek, IR£35 per day. Saturday and Sunday IR£30 per round.
Hire facilities:	**B**
Practice ground:	Full length practice ground
Catering:	Snack bar available at all times from 10.00am. Dining facilities at busy times or by arrangement.

Score card details

Hole	1	2	3	4	5	6	7	8	9	10	11	12	13	14	15	16	17	18
Yds	396	363	405	320	336	300	403	282	159	500	284	379	191	315	507	140	366	407
Par	4	4	4	4	4	4	4	4	3	5	4	4	3	4	5	3	4	4

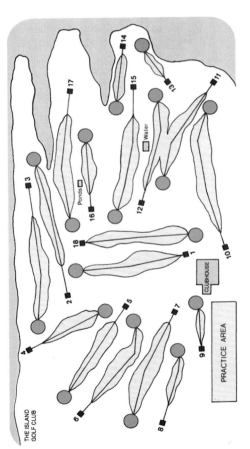

The Island Golf Club: course plan

KILLINEY GOLF CLUB
(ESTABLISHED 1903)
Ballinclea Road, Killiney, Co. Dublin

Nine-hole parkland course in very scenic setting.

Secretary:	Hugh Keegan Tel 01 2852823
Professional:	Paddy O'Boyle Tel 01 2856294
Type:	Parkland
No of holes:	9 (played from outward and inward tees)
Length:	5626 metres
Par:	69
Visitors:	Visitors welcome
Requirements:	M
Handicap Limits:	None
Restrictions:	All visitors restricted on Monday, Wednesday and Friday and Sunday afternoons.
Parties:	Please contact Secretary
Green fees:	IR£17 per round weekdays, IR£20 per round Sundays and public holidays. No special rates.
Hire facilities:	C T Pc
Practice ground:	Practice ground available
Catering:	Snacks available

KILTERNAN GOLF & COUNTRY CLUB HOTEL

(ESTABLISHED 1987)

Kilternan, Co. Dublin

Eighteen-hole hillside course, around hotel.

Secretary:	Jimmy Kinsella, Club Director Tel 01 2955559 Fax 01 2955670
Professional:	None at present
Type:	Parkland
No of holes:	18
Length:	4952 metres
Par:	68
Visitors:	Visitors welcome
Requirements:	None
Handicap Limits:	Gentlemen 24; Ladies 36; Juniors 36
Restrictions:	Course available for all visitors outside competition times. Advance booking required.
Parties:	Please contact Jimmy Kinsella
Green fees:	IR£16 per round Saturday and Sunday. IR£12 per round Monday to Friday.
Hire facilities:	▣ C ▣ T
Practice ground:	None
Catering:	Full catering facilities available

LUCAN GOLF CLUB
(ESTABLISHED 1897)
Celbridge Road, Lucan, Co. Dublin

Good eighteen-hole parkland course. Notable hole is the 4th, par 3, where tee shot crosses main road.

Secretary:	Tom O'Donnell Tel 01 6282106
	Fax 01 6282929
Professional:	None
Type:	Parkland
No of holes:	18
Length:	5650 metres
Par:	71
Visitors:	Visitors welcome
Requirements:	None
Handicap Limits:	None
Restrictions:	All visitors tee times by arrangement with Golf Steward on 01 6280246
Parties:	Please contact Secretary
Green fees:	IR£16 per round
Hire facilities:	
Practice ground:	Practice facilities available
Catering:	Bar snacks. Full catering in summer.

LUTTRELLSTOWN CASTLE GOLF CLUB
(ESTABLISHED 1993)
Clonsilla, Dublin, Co. Dublin

Set in a 560-acre parkland estate, this new championship course -
acclaimed as one of the finest golf venues in the country - has already been
chosen to host part of the Irish Inter-County championships and other
major competitions. From the tiger tees the course is 7091 yards and there
are three other sets of tees for medal rounds, societies and ladies. The
designers have nominated the 3rd, 7th and 12th as the signature holes as
water comes into play, although every hole offers its own unique
challenge. The course is surrounded by scenery of unparalleled beauty.

Secretary:	Maura O'Riordan Tel 01 8208210
	Fax 01 8213241
Professional:	None
Type:	Parkland
No of holes:	18
Length:	6032 metres
Par:	72
Visitors:	Visitors welcome
Requirements:	$\boxed{\text{M}}$
Handicap Limits:	None
Restrictions:	All visitors restricted 2.30 - 4.00pm weekdays,
	8.30 - 10.00am and 12.30 to 2.00pm weekends
Parties:	Please contact Maura O'Riordan
Green fees:	IR£30 weekdays, IR£35 weekends (per day)
Hire facilities:	$\boxed{\text{C}}$ $\boxed{\text{T}}$ $\boxed{\text{Ca}}$ $\boxed{\text{B}}$
Practice ground:	Practice ground and putting green
Catering:	Dining and bar facilities

MALAHIDE GOLF CLUB
(ESTABLISHED 1892)
Beechwood, The Grange, Malahide, Co. Dublin

Malahide Golf Club is a twenty-seven-hole complex which opened in its present location in 1989. It was founded in 1892 by Nathaniel Hone, a famous Irish artist. It is a beautiful parkland course requiring accurate play to all of the raised greens, of which a large proportion are bounded by water. This is a unique club with a reputation for friendliness typified by their motto 'A Light Heart and a Cheerful Spirit'.

Secretary:	Mr A. C. Brogan Tel 01 8461611 Fax 01 8461270	
Professional:	Mr D. Barton Tel 01 8460002	
	Course 1: Red/Blue	**Course 2:** Yellow/Blue
Type:	Parkland	Parkland
No of holes:	18	9 (played from outward and inward tees)
Length:	6619 yards	6257 yards
Par:	71	70
Visitors:	Visitors welcome	
Requirements:	H M	
Handicap Limits:	Gentlemen 28; Ladies 36; Juniors 24	
Restrictions:	Gentlemen restricted on Tuesday and Sunday morning. Ladies restricted Saturday and Sunday. Juniors must be accompanied by an adult after 5.00pm.	
Parties:	Contact Mr A. C. Brogan	
Green fees:	Midweek IR£21. Weekends IR£31. Special rates for groups of 20 and over.	
Hire facilities:	C Ca B	
Practice ground:	None	
Catering:	Full restaurant facilities and bar	

Malahide Golf Club

MILLTOWN GOLF CLUB
(ESTABLISHED 1907)
Lower Churchtown Road, Milltown, Dublin 14

Attractive eighteen-hole parkland course. Central location.

Secretary:	William Johnston, Manager Tel 01 4976090
	Fax 01 4976008
Professional:	John Harnett Tel 01 4977072
Type:	Parkland
No of holes:	18
Length:	5638 metres
Par:	71
Visitors:	Visitors welcome
Requirements:	H M
Handicap Limits:	None
Restrictions:	Always check with Professional
Parties:	Arrange with Mr. William Johnston
Green fees:	IR£30 per round
Hire facilities:	Ca T
Practice ground:	Driving and putting area. (Check with Professional.)
Catering:	Full bar open regular opening hours. Large dining room (seating capacity 200). Three private suites seating 100, 25, 20.

NEWLANDS GOLF CLUB
(ESTABLISHED 1926)
Clondalkin, Dublin 22

The course is a mature parkland course designed by James Braid. It is conveniently located five miles from the city centre on the N7 at Newlands Cross, adjacent to the Green Isle Hotel.

Secretary:	Mr A. T. O'Neill, Secretary/Manager
	Tel 01 4593157 Fax 01 4593498
Professional:	Karl O'Donnell Tel 01 4593538
Type:	Parkland
No of holes:	18
Length:	5714 metres
Par:	71
Visitors:	Visitors welcome
Requirements:	None
Handicap Limits:	None
Restrictions:	Ladies and Gentlemen may play Monday, Thursday and Friday all day (excluding 1.30 - 2.30). Other days by arrangement and subject to competitions etc.
Parties:	Please contact Secretary/Manager
Green fees:	IR£25 per round. Societies IR£23.
Hire facilities:	**T**
Practice ground:	Practice ground, net and putting green
Catering:	Full catering facilities 10.00am - 9.30pm

PORTMARNOCK GOLF CLUB

(ESTABLISHED 1894)

Portmarnock, Co. Dublin

1894 - 1994

Situated 10 miles north of Dublin city centre, this world-famous links has hosted many major championships and was for some years the venue for the Carrolls Irish Open. Portmarnock remains in perfect playing condition throughout the year and is a very popular choice with visitors to Ireland.

Secretary:	John J. Quigley Tel 01 8462968 Fax 01 8462601
Professional:	Joey Purcell Tel 01 8462634
Type:	Links
No of holes:	18
Length:	6497 metres
Par:	72
Visitors:	Visitors welcome
Requirements:	H M
Handicap Limits:	Gentlemen 28; Ladies 36
Restrictions:	Visitors restricted weekdays from 9.30 - 10.00am and 12.30 - 2.30pm. Also Saturdays, Sundays and public holidays, except after 3.30pm in summer period.
Parties:	Please contact John J. Quigley in writing
Green fees:	IR£40 per day or per round weekdays. IR£50 Saturday and Sunday and Public Holidays subject to availability.
Hire facilities:	C T Ca B
Practice ground:	None stated
Catering:	Full catering facilities (must be booked in advance for groups of 12 or more)

Portmarnock Golf Club

ROYAL DUBLIN GOLF CLUB

(ESTABLISHED 1885)

Bull Island, Dollymount, Dublin 3

The club is located on the north-east coast of Dublin approximately four miles from the city centre and 15 minutes' drive from Dublin Airport. It has hosted numerous championship events including the Irish Open and Carrolls Irish Open. The 18th hole (par 4) demands a shot over the out of bounds to reach the green in two strokes.

Secretary:	John A. Lambe, Secretary/Manager Tel 01 8336346 Fax 01 8336504
Professional:	Leonard Owens Tel 01 8336477

	Course 1: White (Blue - Championship)	**Course 2:** Yellow (Red - Ladies)
Type:	Links	Links
No of holes:	18	18
Length:	6016 metres	5755 metres
Par:	72	70

Visitors:	Visitors welcome
Requirements:	Under review
Handicap Limits:	None
Restrictions:	Visitors restricted on Club competition days and on other days 8.30 - 9.30am and 12.30 - 2.00pm — reserved for members. Alternate Sundays visitors 10.30 - 12.30. Juniors: please phone for details.
Parties:	Please contact Secretary/Manager
Green fees:	IR£35 per round, IR£52.50 per day weekdays. Saturday and Sunday IR£45.
Hire facilities:	C T Ca
Practice ground:	Practice ground near clubhouse
Catering:	Formal restaurant and golfers' snack bar. Early closing on Mondays in winter.

Royal Dublin Golf Club

ST. ANNE'S GOLF CLUB
(ESTABLISHED 1921)
North Bull Island, Dollymount, Dublin 5

St. Anne's is a links course situated on The Bull Island on the north side of Dublin Bay. It is four miles from the centre of Dublin city. St. Anne's is a flat course with all-year-round golf.

Secretary:	Mr J. Carberry, Secretary/Manager
	Tel 01 8336471
Professional:	Mr P. Skerritt Tel 01 8314138
Type:	Links
No of holes:	18
Length:	5797 metres
Par:	70
Visitors:	Visitors welcome
Requirements:	None
Handicap Limits:	None
Restrictions:	Restrictions only during competitions
Parties:	Please contact Mr J. Carberry, Secretary/Manager
Green fees:	IR£20 weekdays, IR£25 weekends per round.
	Special rates by arrangement for over 40 players.
Hire facilities:	🎀
Practice ground:	Practice ground available
Catering:	Full catering available

SKERRIES GOLF CLUB
(ESTABLISHED 1906)

Hacketstown, Skerries, Co. Dublin

A parkland course which has superb views of the coastline. The highlights of the course are probably the 12th (par 3) and the 18th (par 4) holes.

Secretary:	Aiden Burns, Secretary/Manager
	Tel 01 8491567
Professional:	Jimmy Kinsella Tel 01 8490925
Type:	Parkland
No of holes:	18
Length:	6113 metres
Par:	73
Visitors:	Visitors welcome
Requirements:	H
Handicap Limits:	Gentlemen 20; Ladies 20; Juniors 9
Restrictions:	All visitors must make prior applications
Parties:	Please contact Aiden Burns, Secretary/Manager
Green fees:	IR£17 per round. Special rates for societies negotiable.
Hire facilities:	C T Pc B
Practice ground:	Adequate practice facilities
Catering:	Full catering and bar service

SLADE VALLEY GOLF CLUB
(ESTABLISHED 1970)

Lynch Park, Brittas, Co. Dublin

Slade Valley
Golf Club
Founded 1970

Located in the Dublin mountains about nine miles west of Dublin city, this is probably one of the highest golf courses in Ireland. It is a very hilly course, but a great challenge to golfing skills. The clubhouse offers first-class hospitality and visitors are most welcome. Caddies are available by arrangement.

Secretary:	Patrick Maguire Tel 01 4582739
Professional:	John Dignam Tel 01 4582183
Type:	Parkland
No of holes:	18
Length:	5337 metres
Par:	69
Visitors:	Visitors welcome
Requirements:	None
Handicap Limits:	Gentlemen 28; Ladies 36; Juniors 36
Restrictions:	All visitors restricted on Saturdays and Sundays
Parties:	Please contact Secretary, Patrick Maguire
Green fees:	IR£15 per round. No special rates.
Hire facilities:	**C** **T** **Ca** (on request) **B**
Practice ground:	None
Catering:	Full catering service 11.00am – 12.00pm

STACKSTOWN GOLF CLUB
(ESTABLISHED 1976)
Kellystown Road, Rathfarnham, Dublin 16

This is a parkland course set in the foothills of the Dublin mountains and overlooking Dublin city, with spectacular views of the surrounding city and countryside. The course is a good test of golf with the front nine holes relatively flat and the back nine relatively hilly. The club has a very good reputation for hospitality and there are two full-size snooker tables. The restaurant is situated to take in the full view of Dublin, which is a spectacular sight at night.

Secretary:	Kieran Lawler, Sec.; Laurence McCormack, Hon. Sec. Tel 01 4942338/4941993
Professional:	Michael Kavanagh Tel 01 4944561
Type:	Parkland
No of holes:	18
Length:	5952 metres
Par:	72
Visitors:	Visitors welcome
Requirements:	None
Handicap Limits:	None
Restrictions:	Always contact Club Sec. or Professional to check availability. No restrictions Monday to Friday except when societies have booked. Avoid Saturdays and club competitions.
Parties:	Contact Club Secretary and Club Steward
Green fees:	IR£14 per round weekdays, IR£18 Saturday and Sunday
Hire facilities:	C (limited) T
Practice ground:	Short practice ground - being enlarged now.
Catering:	Full catering facilities available 10.00am - 10.00pm daily

SUTTON GOLF CLUB
(ESTABLISHED 1890)
Cush Point, Burrow Road, Sutton, Dublin 13

Sutton golf course is a nine-hole links course located seven miles east of Dublin. Established in 1890, Sutton has produced ten Irish International players, the most famous being J. B. Carr, Captain of the R & A 1991/1992. Surrounded on two sides by the Irish Sea, visitors will find Sutton a rare challenge.

Secretary:	Hugh O'Neill Tel 01 8323013
Professional:	Nick Lynch Tel 01 8321603
Type:	Links
No of holes:	9
Length:	2859 yards
Par:	34
Visitors:	Visitors welcome
Requirements:	None
Handicap Limits:	None
Restrictions:	Restrictions apply to all visitors all day Tuesdays and Saturdays before 5.30pm
Parties:	Please contact Hugh O'Neill
Green fees:	IR£15 per round, IR£20 per round weekends. No special rates.
Hire facilities:	🅣
Practice ground:	No practice ground
Catering:	Catering and dining facilities by arrangement

BODENSTOWN GOLF CLUB
(ESTABLISHED 1973)
Bodenstown, Sallins, Co. Kildare

Bodenstown Golf Club has two excellent courses: the 'Old Course' was opened in 1973 by Charles Haughey and 'Ladyhill' came on stream in 1983. The Old Course is one of the finest inland tests of golf in Leinster, designed by Eddie Hackett. Ladyhill is maturing into a fine course and is used mainly for society and greenfee golf.

Secretary:	Peadar Cunningham Tel 045 76588	
Professional:	None	
	Course 1:	**Course 2:**
	Old Course	Ladyhill
Type:	Parkland	Parkland
No of holes:	18	18
Length:	5788 metres	5428 metres
Par:	72	71

Visitors:	Visitors welcome
Requirements:	None
Handicap Limits:	None
Restrictions:	No green fees on Old Course Saturdays and Sundays before 4.00pm
Parties:	Please contact Bernadette Curtin on 045 97096
Green fees:	IR£10 per round. IR£8 per round on Ladyhill at weekends. Daily rates by negotiation.
Hire facilities:	T
Practice ground:	Practice ground available
Catering:	Full catering facilities available seven days per week from 10.00am to 10.00pm

CASTLEWARDEN GOLF AND COUNTRY CLUB
(ESTABLISHED 1990)
Castlewarden, Straffan, Co. Kildare

New eighteen-hole parkland course.

Secretary:	John Ferriter Tel 045 89254
Professional:	Gerry Egan Tel 045 88219
Type:	Parkland
No of holes:	18
Length:	6008 metres
Par:	72
Visitors:	Visitors welcome
Requirements:	None
Handicap Limits:	None
Restrictions:	All visitors restricted on Tuesdays, Wednesdays, Saturdays and Sundays up to 3.00pm
Parties:	Please contact Club Office. No societies on Tuesdays or Sundays.
Green fees:	IR£12 per day (IR£8 with member)
Hire facilities:	C T B
Practice ground:	40 acre practice facilities
Catering:	Bar and restaurant available

THE CURRAGH GOLF CLUB

(ESTABLISHED 1883)

Curragh Camp, Co. Kildare

The Curragh Golf Club possesses the oldest golf course in Ireland, laid out in 1852 by David Ritchie of Musselburgh. Other 1850s golfers included the Earl of Eglinton (Captain, Prestwick 1851 and R & A 1853) and Lt. Col. William Campbell (Captain, Prestwick 1854). The present golf club was founded in 1883, when the Highland Light Infantry was stationed in the adjoining military camp. A new clubhouse has recently been completed.

Secretary:	Ann Culleton Tel 045 41714
Professional:	Phil Lawlor Tel 045 41896
Type:	Heathland
No of holes:	18
Length:	6605 yards (6003 metres)
Par:	72
Visitors:	Visitors welcome
Requirements:	None
Handicap Limits:	None
Restrictions:	Juniors should be accompanied. In general avoid weekends and Tuesdays. Visitors must contact club prior to arrival to check.
Parties:	Must contact Secretary in advance to reserve tee. A deposit will be charged.
Green fees:	IR£14 per round weekdays, IR£18 per round weekends and public holidays. No daily or special rates.

Hire facilities: C   T   Ca

Practice ground: Full practice ground

Catering: Full catering facilities

KILLEEN GOLF CLUB
(ESTABLISHED 1986)
Kill, Co. Kildare

Killeen Golf Club is set in the scenic and peaceful countryside of County Kildare. The eighteen-hole course will challenge the skills of both the moderate enthusiast and the more experienced golfer alike. The club is only a 20-minute drive from Dublin. A comprehensive range of facilities is offered, including a bar, restaurant and function room (with seating for 250 people) and parking for 300 cars.

Secretary:	Peter Carey Tel 045 66003 Fax 045 75881
Professional:	None
Type:	Parkland
No of holes:	18
Length:	5452 yards (4989 metres)
Par:	69
Visitors:	Visitors welcome
Requirements:	None
Handicap Limits:	Gentlemen 24; Ladies 36; Juniors 30
Restrictions:	Time sheet in operation - telephone Secretary to arrange date and time.
Parties:	Contact Peter Carey, Secretary
Green fees:	Green fees on application
Hire facilities:	C T
Practice ground:	Net and putting green
Catering:	Facilities available

KILDARE HOTEL AND COUNTRY CLUB

(ESTABLISHED 1991)

Straffan, Co. Kildare

* * * * *

The club course provides four different tee positions, the longest being the Palmer (6419 metres) down to the Yellow (Visitors) Tees (5683 metres). The layout was designed by Arnold Palmer and his team, led by Ed Seay, and cleverly uses the existing woodland and water. Arnold Palmer believes that the golfer should be challenged from the first tee shot down to the final green. At the same time the course should be fair and enjoyable to play. These objectives have been achieved. The course has already hosted the 1993 Irish Professional Golf Championship.

Secretary:	Ken Greene, Director of Golf Tel 01 627333 Fax 01 6273312
Professional:	Ernie Jones. Tel 01 627333
Type:	Parkland
No of holes:	18
Length:	6368 metres
Par:	72
Visitors:	Visitors welcome
Requirements:	H
Handicap Limits:	Gentlemen 28; Ladies 36
Restrictions:	Restricted tee times are Sunday and Monday 1.30 - 2.30pm and Saturday 10.30 - 3.00pm.
Parties:	Contact Director of Golf, Ken Greene
Green fees:	IR£85 per round of per day. Groups of 16 or more IR£55. Hotel residents IR£55 per day.
Hire facilities:	C T Ca B
Practice ground:	Three practice holes, eighteen-hole putting, driving bay.
Catering:	The snack bar caters for the golfer before and after golf with snacks, and the restaurant provides buffet lunches and *à la carte* dinners.

The K Club (Kildare Hotel & Country Club): clubhouse

Score card details

Hole	1	2	3	4	5	6	7	8	9	10	11	12	13	14	15	16	17	18
Yds	512	351	148	351	177	376	543	306	392	364	361	132	497	358	376	339	140	460
Par	5	4	3	4	3	4	5	4	4	4	4	3	5	4	4	4	3	5

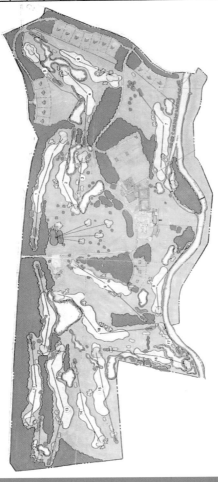

The K Club (Kildare Hotel & Country Club): course plan from White tees

KNOCKANALLY GOLF & COUNTRY CLUB
(ESTABLISHED 1985)
Donadea, North Kildare, Co. Kildare

This championship eighteen-hole golf course stands in 120 acres of parkland with fine scenic views of the Kildare countryside. The clubhouse is a fine Palladian mansion and commands a panoramic view of the entire course. Designed, built and managed by Noel Lyons, this privately owned golf course specially caters for the visitor. Host to the Irish International Professional Matchplay Championship (1987/88/89) and the Irish Club Professional Championship (1994), it offers a challenge to any category of golfer.

Secretary:	Noel Lyons Tel 045 69322
Professional:	Peter Hickey Tel 045 69322
Type:	Parkland
No of holes:	18
Length:	6424 yards
Par:	72
Visitors:	Visitors welcome
Requirements:	None
Handicap Limits:	None
Restrictions:	No restrictions
Parties:	Please contact Noel Lyons
Green fees:	IR£20 per round, IR£30 per day. Special rates by arrangement.

Hire facilities: C   T   Ca

Practice ground: Sizeable practice ground
Catering: Full catering facilities - parties welcome

Knockanally Golf Club

KILKENNY GOLF CLUB
(ESTABLISHED 1896)
Glendine, Co. Kilkenny

The course is of championship standard, set in 120 acres of parkland. It hosted the Carroll's Irish Matchplay Professional Championship in 1973 and in 1984 was the venue for the All Ireland Mixed Foursomes Final. The course is mostly flat terrain with an abundance of trees. Notable features are its four par 3s, the long par 4 11th hole and the final four holes, which have often ruined a fine score. A feature of the course is the 'Fulacht Fiadh', an ancient Irish kitchen. This type of kitchen dates back to the Bronze Age. Visitors will find the golf club, like the city, very friendly.

Secretary:	Sean O'Neill, Manager Tel 056 65400
Professional:	Noel Leahy Tel 056 61730
Type:	Parkland
No of holes:	18
Length:	6450 yards
Par:	71
Visitors:	Visitors welcome
Requirements:	M
Handicap Limits:	Gentlemen 28; Ladies 36; Juniors 36
Restrictions:	None
Parties:	Please contact Secretary/Manager
Green fees:	IR£15 per day weekdays, IR£17 weekends
Hire facilities:	C T Ca
Practice ground:	Two practice grounds and chipping area
Catering:	Facilities available

MOUNT JULIET GOLF CLUB
(ESTABLISHED 1991)
Thomastown, Co. Kilkenny

Mount Juliet golf course nestles amid rolling green landscapes, magnificent scenery and the unspoilt beauty of County Kilkenny. The eighteen-hole Jack Nicklaus Signature Course is acclaimed as one of the country's top courses and the home of the Irish Open for the past two years. There is also the opportunity to improve your game at the David Leadbetter Golfing Academy.

Secretary:	Eoin Gahan Tel 056 24725 Fax 056 24522
Professional:	David Leadbetter Golf Academy staff Tel 056 24725 Fax 056 24022
Type:	Parkland
No of holes:	18
Length:	7101 yards (6493 metres)
Par:	72
Visitors:	Visitors welcome
Requirements:	H
Handicap Limits:	Gentlemen 28; Ladies 36
Restrictions:	Hotel residents have priority between 9.00 - 10.00am and 1.00 - 2.00pm
Parties:	Please contact Ms Phil Lanigan on 056 24725 ext. 212
Green fees:	IR£60 per round, IR£90 per day. Special rates for residents and groups.
Hire facilities:	C T Ca
Practice ground:	Large practice ground including putting green
Catering:	Loft Restaurant in clubhouse. Bar/catering - Presidents Bar and Spike Bar.

Mount Juliet Golf Club

HEATH (PORTLAOISE) GOLF CLUB
(ESTABLISHED 1889)
The Heath, Portlaoise, Co. Laois

Heath offers year-round golf and is particularly dry in winter. The course incorporates three natural lakes and offers spectacular views of the hills of Laois. With its rough of heather and gorse furze, it is a challenge for any golfer. A fully illuminated driving range provides an excellent practice area. The club is situated three miles east of Portlaoise, adjacent to the main Dublin to Cork and Limerick road and less than an hour from Dublin.

Secretary:	Patrick A. Malone Tel 0502 21074 (home)
Professional:	Eddie Doyle Tel 0502 46622
Type:	Semi-links
No of holes:	18
Length:	5736 metres
Par:	71
Visitors:	Visitors welcome
Requirements:	H M
Handicap Limits:	None stated
Restrictions:	Varies depending on competitions - please telephone. Juniors not allowed after 5.00pm.
Parties:	Contact Thomas Tyrrell (Society Secretary) c/o Heath Golf Club
Green fees:	IR£10 per round midweek, IR£16 weekends and public holidays
Hire facilities:	C T
Practice ground:	Driving range and putting green
Catering:	Full catering facilities

PORTARLINGTON GOLF CLUB
(ESTABLISHED 1909)
Garryhinch, Portarlington, Co. Laois

Founded 1909

The course is designed around a setting of mature trees. There is a river flowing through the course which, gives a very challenging finishing section. There are also a number of ponds which come into play and add to the difficulty, but also enhance the very scenic setting.

Secretary:	Michael J. Turley Tel 0502 23115
	Fax 0502 23734
Professional:	None
Type:	Parkland
No of holes:	18
Length:	6206 yards (5673 metres)
Par:	71
Visitors:	Visitors welcome
Requirements:	**H** (competitions only)
Handicap Limits:	None
Restrictions:	Tuesday is Ladies Day and Ladies have priority. Saturday and Sunday very difficult for all visitors. Juniors must have round completed by 12.00 noon.
Parties:	Contact the Club Secretary - essential to book well in advance.
Green fees:	IR£10 per round, IR£12 weekends and public holidays. No daily rates.
Hire facilities:	**T**
Practice ground:	Practice fairway and green
Catering:	Full catering and dining available at the club by reservation

COUNTY LONGFORD GOLF CLUB

(ESTABLISHED 1894)

Glack, Dublin Road, Longford, Co. Longford

The course is centrally located, and just over an hour from Dublin. It enjoys panoramic views of the surrounding countryside and is extremely well-drained, so play is possible twelve months of the year - almost unique for an inland course. The area is heavily wooded and the many mature trees provide a beautiful backdrop to all the holes. There is a choice of high quality hotels and guest houses within walking distance of the course and a full range of meals is available in the modern new clubhouse.

Secretary:	Mr A. Mitchell Tel 043 46310
Professional:	None
Type:	Parkland
No of holes:	18
Length:	6044 yards
Par:	72
Visitors:	Visitors welcome
Requirements:	None
Handicap Limits:	Gentlemen 24; Ladies 36; Juniors 36
Restrictions:	None
Parties:	Please contact John Donlon
Green fees:	IR£10 weekdays, IR£12 weekends per round. Special rates for groups and members' guests.
Hire facilities:	C T B
Practice ground:	None
Catering:	Bar and dining facilities

Co. Longford Golf Club: views

ARDEE GOLF CLUB
(ESTABLISHED 1911)
Townparks, Ardee, Co. Louth

Eighteen-hole course in treelined parkland setting with trees and stream as additional feature.

Secretary:	Seamus Kelly Tel 041 53227/56283
	Fax 041 56153
Professional:	None
Type:	Parkland
No of holes:	18
Length:	6200 yards
Par:	69
Visitors:	Visitors welcome
Requirements:	None
Handicap Limits:	Gentlemen 28; Ladies 36; Juniors: varies
Restrictions:	None
Parties:	Please contact Seamus Kelly
Green fees:	IR£15 per day. IR£13 for societies midweek.
Hire facilities:	🇹 🇨a 🇧
Practice ground:	Practice area available
Catering:	Catering facilities available

COUNTY LOUTH GOLF CLUB
(ESTABLISHED 1892)
Baltray, Drogheda, Co. Louth

The course at County Louth, known as Baltray, is reckoned to be one of the best in Ireland. There are two fine opening holes and then a classic seaside par 5. Some slight respite follows in the shape of a drive and pitch 4th, but the 5th introduces players to the first of the four short holes - all confronting the wind from different directions. The 5th and 7th have their greens nestling in the sandhills but the 6th is another par 5, followed by two splendid two-shotters. The excitement of the second nine centres on the holes close to the sea and the Mountains of Mourne.

Secretary:	Michael Delaney Tel 041 22329 Fax 041 22969
Professional:	Paddy McGuirk Tel 041 22444
Type:	Links
No of holes:	18
Length:	6728 yards
Par:	73
Visitors:	Visitors welcome
Requirements:	H M
Handicap Limits:	Gentlemen 28; Ladies 36
Restrictions:	No visitors Tuesdays and weekends
Parties:	Apply to Secretary
Green fees:	IR£27 per round or per day
Hire facilities:	C T Ca
Practice ground:	Practice ground available
Catering:	Full bar and restaurant facilities

Co. Louth Golf Club: clubhouse and view

Score card details

Hole	1	2	3	4	5	6	7	8	9	10	11	12	13	14	15	16	17	18
Yds	433	476	544	344	158	531	163	407	419	398	481	410	421	332	152	388	179	492
Par	4	5	5	4	3	5	3	4	4	4	5	4	4	4	3	4	3	5

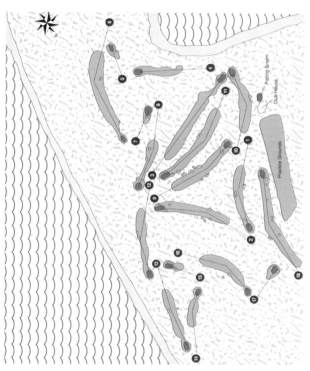

Co. Louth Golf Club: course plan

DUNDALK GOLF CLUB
(ESTABLISHED 1896)
Blackrock, Dundalk, Co. Louth

Attractive and improving eighteen-hole parkland course.

Secretary:	Joe Carroll Tel 042 21731 Fax 042 22022
Professional:	James Cassidy Tel 042 22102
Type:	Parkland
No of holes:	18
Length:	6776 yards (6160 metres)
Par:	72
Visitors:	Visitors welcome
Requirements:	None
Handicap Limits:	Gentlemen 28; Ladies 36; Juniors - please check
Restrictions:	Tuesday is Ladies Day. Gentlemen welcome on Monday, Wednesday, Thursday and Friday.
Parties:	Please contact Secretary
Green fees:	IR£16 per day or per round. No special rates.
Hire facilities:	C T B
Practice ground:	Eight-acre field
Catering:	Full catering facilities

GREENORE GOLF CLUB

(ESTABLISHED 1896)

Greenore, Co. Louth

A beautiful, scenic eighteen-hole links course situated on the shores of Carlingford Lough with picturesque views of the Mourne Mountains. It is a challenge to the lowest of handicaps with a spectacular par 3 6th hole surrounded by water and sand bunkers; a very interesting course well worth a visit. You can relax in the comfort of the new clubhouse lounge and enjoy the panoramic views. Caddies available on prior request.

Secretary:	Mrs Roisin Daly Tel 042 73212 Fax 042 73678
Professional:	None
Type:	Links
No of holes:	18
Length:	6506 yards
Par:	71
Visitors:	Visitors welcome
Requirements:	None: competitions only
Handicap Limits:	Gentlemen 20; Ladies 28
Restrictions:	Visitors welcome at all times - prior booking advisable from May to September
Parties:	Please contact Roisin Daly - society tee reservations by prior arrangement Saturday 10.30 - 11.45am and Sunday 11.45am - 1.00pm
Green fees:	IR£12 per round Monday to Friday. IR£18 per round Saturday, Sunday and public holidays.
Hire facilities:	⊤ C
Practice ground:	None
Catering:	Full catering facilities: breakfast/lunch/*à-la-carte*/bar snacks

SEAPOINT GOLF CLUB
(ESTABLISHED 1993)
Termonfeckin, Co. Louth

A course designed and built by Des Smyth and Associates in 1990; because of the nature of links grasses it has taken three years to mature. It requires some big carries off the tee and contains some tough par 3s. A concentrated effort is required to play this championship course and concentration will be rewarded.

Secretary:	Amelia Smith Tel 041 22333
Professional:	David Carroll Tel 041 22333
Type:	Links
No of holes:	18
Length:	6339 metres
Par:	72
Visitors:	Visitors welcome
Requirements:	H M
Handicap Limits:	None
Restrictions:	Members time 1.00 - 2.00pm each day
Parties:	Please contact David Carroll, Professional
Green fees:	IR£17 per round
Hire facilities:	T Ca B
Practice ground:	Practice ground available
Catering:	Excellent restaurant and bar facilities

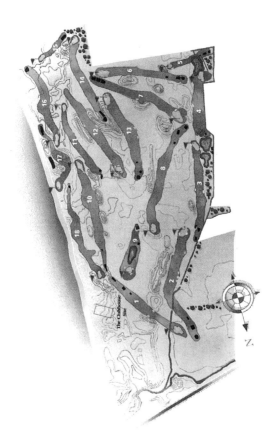

Seapoint Golf Club: course plan

HEADFORT GOLF CLUB
(ESTABLISHED 1928)
Kells, Co. Meath

Eighteen-hole parkland course in lovely countryside.

Secretary:	Edward Carolan Tel 046 40857
Professional:	Brendan McGovern Tel 046 40639
Type:	Parkland
No of holes:	18
Length:	6480 yards
Par:	72
Visitors:	Visitors welcome
Requirements:	H M
Handicap Limits:	Gentlemen 28; Ladies 36
Restrictions:	No visitors before 12.30pm Monday, Wednesday, Thursday and Friday. Prior notice essential to ensure reservations.
Parties:	Contact Secretary
Green fees:	IR£15 per round weekday, IR£18 weekends
Hire facilities:	C T Ca
Practice ground:	Practice area available
Catering:	Full catering facilities

LAYTOWN AND BETTYSTOWN GOLF CLUB
(ESTABLISHED 1909)
Bettystown, Co. Meath

L.B.G.C.

Laytown and Bettystown Golf Club is situated about 30 miles north of Dublin Airport. The links run along the sea shore. The course is open 365 days a year and green fees are always welcome; however, it is best to ring beforehand.

Secretary:	Stella Garvey-Hoey Tel 041 27170
Professional:	Mr R. J. Browne Tel 041 27563
Type:	Links
No of holes:	18
Length:	5668 metres
Par:	72
Visitors:	Visitors welcome
Requirements:	None
Handicap Limits:	Gentlemen 28; Ladies 36
Restrictions:	No green fees on Saturdays and Sundays from October to March. Tee times available weekdays but it is always better to ring for a tee time.
Parties:	Please contact Stella Garvey-Hoey: group rates available for parties of over 20
Green fees:	IR£17 weekdays, IR£22 weekends
Hire facilities:	C T
Practice ground:	None
Catering:	Bar/restaurant facilities available

ROYAL TARA GOLF CLUB
(ESTABLISHED 1923)
Bellinter, Navan, Co. Meath

This is a lovely eighteen-hole parkland course designed by Des Smyth.

Secretary:	Patrick O'Brien Tel 046 25508
Professional:	Adam Whiston Tel 046 25244
Type:	Parkland
No of holes:	18
Length:	5904 yards
Par:	72
Visitors:	Visitors welcome
Requirements:	H (competitions only)
Handicap Limits:	None
Restrictions:	Ladies Day Tuesday
Parties:	Contact Secretary or Professional on 046 26009
Green fees:	IR£14 per round; IR£18 per round weekends
Hire facilities:	C T B
Practice ground:	None
Catering:	Full bar and catering facilities - all day summer, restricted in winter

TRIM GOLF CLUB
(ESTABLISHED 1898)
Newtownmoynagh, Trim, Co. Meath

This eighteen-hole parkland course has 40 sand bunkers, two grass bunkers and 24 water hazards together with 20 acres of trees. It will provide a challenge to all levels of golfing ability. The present comfortable clubhouse has been an attractive feature of the club since it was built in 1970 and plays a major part in building the great social atmosphere. Trim Golf Club provides a genuine Irish welcome for members and visitors alike.

Secretary:	Peter J. Darby Tel 046 31438
Professional:	None
Type:	Parkland
No of holes:	18
Length:	6820 yards
Par:	73
Visitors:	Visitors welcome
Requirements:	None
Handicap Limits:	None
Restrictions:	Restrictions apply on Saturdays, Sundays and Thursdays. It is advisable to telephone Club at all times for appointments.
Parties:	Please contact Hon. Sec. Trim Golf Club for appointment/booking
Green fees:	IR£12 per round midweek, IR£15 weekends
Hire facilities:	T B
Practice ground:	Large practice area - 7 acres
Catering:	Full catering available at all times

BIRR GOLF CLUB
(ESTABLISHED 1893)
Glenns, Birr, Co. Offaly

The course is undulating parkland with some difficult holes. It is situated about two miles from Birr on the Banagher Road. The club is very popular with societies who are always well catered for.

Secretary:	Eamonn Connolly Tel 0509 20656/20082
Professional:	None
Type:	Parkland
No of holes:	18
Length:	5748 metres
Par:	70
Visitors:	Visitors welcome
Requirements:	None
Handicap Limits:	Gentlemen 26
Restrictions:	Visitors generally unrestricted - except Saturdays and Sundays when booking is advised
Parties:	Please contact Hon. Sec. Eamonn Connolly
Green fees:	IR£10 per round
Hire facilities:	🅣
Practice ground:	None
Catering:	Full bar and dining facilities

TULLAMORE GOLF CLUB
(ESTABLISHED 1886)
Brookfield, Tullamore, Co. Offaly

First established in 1886, the present eighteen-hole course was opened at
Brookfield in 1926. It was extended in 1938 by James Braid to produce the
course which exists today. It is in mature parkland and has many clusters
of trees and dense avenues, with a stream running through against the
backdrop of the Slieve Bloom mountains. Visiting golfers are welcome
and 'Open' competitions are held in the summer months, with an 'Open
Week' in the first week of June each year. The course is located three
miles south-west of the town on the Kinnity Road.

Secretary:	Hon. Sec. Aidan Marsden
	Tel 0506 51317 (home)
Professional:	Donagh McArdle Tel and Fax 0506 51757
Type:	Parkland
No of holes:	18
Length:	5779 metres
Par:	71
Visitors:	Visitors welcome
Requirements:	H M
Handicap Limits:	Gentlemen 28; Ladies 36; Juniors 36
Restrictions:	Tee times by arrangement with the Hon. Secretary or Professional
Parties:	Please contact Hon. Sec.
Green fees:	IR£12 per round weekdays, IR£15 weekends and public holidays
Hire facilities:	C T Ca
Practice ground:	Full practice ground on course
Catering:	Full catering facilities available all day all year round. Bar/lounge facilities for visitors.

Tullamore Golf Club: clubhouse

MULLINGAR GOLF CLUB
(ESTABLISHED 1937)
Belvedere, Mullingar, Co. Westmeath

An interesting and testing course on undulating terrain landscaped with
trees, generally recognised as one of James Braid's best designs. Each hole
has its own individual character and there is a wide variety of hazards to
overcome. Mullingar was awarded championship status in 1952 when the
club staged the Irish Professional Championship, and it hosts the
Mullingar Scratch Cup annually. The course is situated three miles south
of Mullingar.

Secretary:	Charles Mulligan, Secretary/Manager
	Tel 044 48366
Professional:	John Burns Tel 044 40085
Type:	Parkland
No of holes:	18
Length:	6200 yards
Par:	72
Visitors:	Visitors welcome
Requirements:	H
Handicap Limits:	None
Restrictions:	Restricted on Wednesdays and weekends. Prior
	arrangements required for weekends.
Parties:	Popular society course - contact Secretary/Manager
Green fees:	IR£16 weekdays and IR£23 weekends and public
	holidays
Hire facilities:	C T B
Practice ground:	None
Catering:	Bar food available

Mullingar Golf Club

COURTOWN GOLF CLUB
(ESTABLISHED 1936)
Courtown Harbour, Kiltennel, Gorey, Co. Wexford

Courtown Golf Club is three miles from Gorey and the N11 national route - 50 miles from Dublin and 35 miles from Rosslare harbour. A parkland course with some spectacular views of the nearby sea through tree-lined fairways. Every hole has unique features, particularly the four par 3s. It is a course to be enjoyed by scratch golfer and beginner alike.

Secretary:	John Finn Tel 055 25166
Professional:	John Coone Tel/Fax 055 25553
Type:	Parkland
No of holes:	18
Length:	5898 metres
Par:	71
Visitors:	Visitors welcome
Requirements:	None
Handicap Limits:	None
Restrictions:	Generally there are no restrictions, but it is best to ring beforehand
Parties:	Contact John Finn
Green fees:	IR£20 weekend and IR£15 midweek in June, July and August. IR£17 weekend and IR£13 midweek September - May.
Hire facilities:	C T
Practice ground:	Good practice ground available
Catering:	Full catering facilities

ENNISCORTHY GOLF CLUB
(ESTABLISHED 1904)
Knockmarshal, Enniscorthy, Co. Wexford

Mature parkland course designed by Eddie Hackett 1¹/₂ miles from
Enniscorthy post office off Enniscorthy/New Ross road. Very favourably
commented on by all visitors, the course has been redesigned and
improved in the last few years.

Secretary:	Hon. Sec., Jim Winters; Sec. Ann Byrne Tel 054 33191
Professional:	None
Type:	Parkland
No of holes:	18
Length:	6266 yards (5697 metres)
Par:	70
Visitors:	Visitors welcome
Requirements:	H M
Handicap Limits:	None
Restrictions:	Prior confirmation with office required in all cases
Parties:	Please contact office
Green fees:	IR£10 midweek, IR£12 weekends and public holidays
Hire facilities:	T
Practice ground:	Pitching and putting practice area
Catering:	Available all day

ROSSLARE GOLF CLUB
(ESTABLISHED 1908)
Rosslare Strand, Rosslare, Co. Wexford

Rosslare provides an excellent test of golf on a championship links beside the Irish Sea. Fairways, tees and greens are watered, giving an enjoyable playing surface in both summer and winter. Dean Beaman (USGA Commissioner) after his round at Rosslare stated that "the wind on this links makes it a great test of golfing skill".

Secretary:	Mr J. F. Hall, Secretary/Manager Tel 053 32203
Professional:	Austin Skerritt Tel 053 32238

	Course 1: Old	**Course 2:** New Nine
Type:	Links	Links
No of holes:	18	9
Length:	6554 yds (5993 m)	3153 yds (2883 m)
Par:	72	35

Visitors:	Visitors welcome
Requirements:	**M**
Handicap Limits:	Gentlemen 28; Ladies 36
Restrictions:	Time sheets in operation Tuesdays, Saturdays and Sundays. Tuesday is Ladies Day. Please ring for booking.
Parties:	Please contact Secretary/Manager for booking
Green fees:	Old Course: IR£18 midweek, IR£23 weekends and public holidays. New Nine: IR£8 for nine holes, IR£12 for eighteen.
Hire facilities:	**C** **T**
Practice ground:	Practice ground available
Catering:	Full catering facilities available

Rosslare Golf Club

WEXFORD GOLF CLUB

(ESTABLISHED 1961)

Mulgannon, Co. Wexford

A parkland course with mature trees and beautiful views of County Wexford including the Saltee Islands, the Blackstairs Mountain Range and Wexford Harbour. It is located within half a mile of Wexford town.

Secretary:	Pat Daly Tel 053 42238
Professional:	Paul Roche Tel 053 46300
Type:	Parkland
No of holes:	18
Length:	6120 yards
Par:	72
Visitors:	Visitors welcome
Requirements:	H M
Handicap Limits:	Gentlemen 28; Ladies 36
Restrictions:	Gentlemen restricted Sundays and Thursdays. Ladies and Juniors restricted on Sundays.
Parties:	Contact Phil Roche (Steward)
Green fees:	IR£14 per round (IR£12 per round low season). Special rates for societies.
Hire facilities:	C T
Practice ground:	No
Catering:	Snacks, soup, etc. Groups by prior arrangement.

ARKLOW GOLF CLUB
(ESTABLISHED 1927)
Abbeylands, Arklow, Co. Wicklow

A typical links course with majestic scenery and the opportunity to play throughout the year. Recent irrigation system installation has enhanced the overall playing surface and the course is a challenge to low and high handicappers alike. The course is located half a mile from Arklow town centre.

Secretary:	Brendan Timmons, Hon. Secretary Tel 0402 32492
Professional:	None
Type:	Links
No of holes:	18
Length:	5404 metres
Par:	68
Visitors:	Visitors welcome
Requirements:	H M
Handicap Limits:	Gentlemen 28; Ladies 36; Juniors 20
Restrictions:	Visitors avoid Monday (Ladies Day) and Sunday (Medal Day). Juniors not allowed at weekend unless with parent.
Parties:	Contact Hon. Secretary - apply in writing with official Golfing Union request
Green fees:	IR£13 per round weekdays, IR£18 per round weekends. Special rates negotiable depending on numbers.
Hire facilities:	Ca T
Practice ground:	Nets. Putting green being built for 1995.
Catering:	Snacks and bar service. Meals may be prearranged with catering contractor.

BLAINROE GOLF CLUB

(ESTABLISHED 1978)

Blainroe, Co. Wicklow

A fine eighteen-hole parkland course on hilly terrain overlooking the Irish Sea. Some water features - 15th hole in particular.

Secretary:	Mr W. O'Sullivan, Manager Tel 0404 68168
	Fax 0404 69369
Professional:	John McDonald Tel 0404 68168
Type:	Parkland
No of holes:	18
Length:	6788 yards (6171 metres)
Par:	72
Visitors:	Visitors welcome
Requirements:	None
Handicap Limits:	Gentlemen 28; Ladies 36; Juniors 36
Restrictions:	Sunday is Men's Competition Day - visitors after 3.30pm. Monday is Ladies Day - visitors after 5.00pm. Juniors, please check.
Parties:	Please contact D. O'Donovan (Club Secretary)
Green fees:	IR£18 per round midweek, IR£25 weekends
Hire facilities:	C T B
Practice ground:	None
Catering:	Full dining facilities

BRAY GOLF CLUB
(ESTABLISHED 1897)
Ravenswell Road, Bray, Co. Wicklow

A nine-hole layout with different tee boxes for each nine, making for an interesting eighteen holes. Situated in the town of Bray, 15 miles from Dublin and close to all hotels and guest houses.

Secretary:	Mr T. Brennan, Secretary/Manager Tel 01 2862484
Professional:	Michael Walby Tel 01 2862092
Type:	Parkland
No of holes:	9 (played from outward and inward tees)
Length:	5761 metres
Par:	69
Visitors:	Visitors welcome
Requirements:	None
Handicap Limits:	None
Restrictions:	Gentlemen and Ladies restricted Saturday, Sunday and Monday, all day. Juniors as above and after 6.00pm weekdays.
Parties:	Please contact Secretary/Manager
Green fees:	IR£17 per round (eighteen holes). No special rates.
Hire facilities:	C T B
Practice ground:	None
Catering:	If requested beforehand, for parties not less than 10

CHARLESLAND GOLF & COUNTRY CLUB HOTEL

(ESTABLISHED 1992)

Greystones, Co. Wicklow

Charlesland is situated just 35-minutes' drive from Dublin city centre and only 30 minutes from Dun Laoghaire Ferry Port. The course was designed by Ireland's foremost golf architect, Eddie Hackett, who says, "I couldn't have asked for a better parkland site". His signature hole is the spectacular short 13th where the tee is the highest point on the course. The hotel has 12 en-suite bedrooms, sauna and jacuzzi. Also an executive board room and conference rooms, ideal for business hospitality.

Secretary:	Madeleine Doherty, Golf Administrator Tel 01 2876764 Fax 01 2873882
Professional:	Paul Heeney Tel as above
Type:	Parkland
No of holes:	18
Length:	6739 yards (6159 metres)
Par:	72
Visitors:	Visitors welcome
Requirements:	None
Handicap Limits:	None
Restrictions:	Visitors welcome every day; restrictions only during competitions, which are mainly at weekends.
Parties:	Contact Madeleine Doherty. Special rates for parties and societies, and hotel guests.
Green fees:	IR£23 per round weekdays, IR£28 weekends
Hire facilities:	C T B
Practice ground:	Practice ground, putting green, driving range
Catering:	Restaurant open Wednesday and Saturday evening and Sunday lunch, also for parties any time by arrangement. Full bar food menu all day and bar licence.

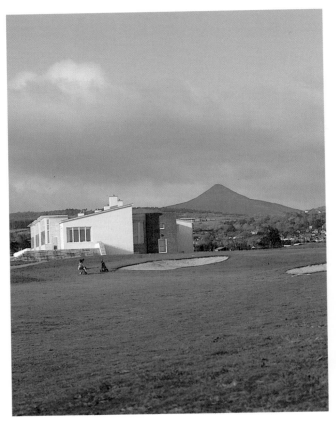

Charlesland Golf Club

DELGANY GOLF CLUB
(ESTABLISHED 1919)
Delgany, Co. Wicklow

A delightful eighteen-hole course with splendid views of the sea,
countryside and mountains. Two or three good hills, parkland with not too
many bunkers. The club has a proud tradition of warm hospitality and
visitors are always welcome.

Secretary:	Mr R. J. Kelly, Secretary/Manager
	Tel 01 2874536/2874833 Fax 01 2873977
Professional:	Eamonn Darcy Tel 01 2874697
Type:	Parkland
No of holes:	18
Length:	5290 metres
Par:	69
Visitors:	Visitors welcome
Requirements:	M
Handicap Limits:	None
Restrictions:	Restricted on Wednesday afternoons, Saturday and Sunday. Ladies also restricted on Tuesdays. Juniors by arrangement.
Parties:	Please contact Secretary/Manager. All society players must be members of another club.
Green fees:	IR£17 per round, IR£25 per day. IR£20 per round weekends (if available). Special rates arranged.
Hire facilities:	C T Ca Pc B
Practice ground:	Available
Catering:	Full catering/dining every day except Monday

THE EUROPEAN GOLF CLUB
(ESTABLISHED 1992)
Brittas Bay, Co. Wicklow

Designed and built by a great lover of the game, Pat Ruddy, the links of the European Club (the first to be built on Ireland's east coast this century) has been ranked No. 7 among Ireland's 30 Greatest Golf Courses by the Irish Golf Institute. It is also ranked No. 5 among the best new courses opened in Britain and Ireland since 1992 by *Golf World*. This is a spectacular links tumbling through the dunes overlooking Arklow Bay and Brittas Bay, just 40 minutes south from the Dublin suburbs. This course is a shrine to golf, and most of the holes are named after famous golfers.

Secretary:	Pat Ruddy Tel 0404 47415 Fax 01 2808457
Professional:	None
Type:	Links
No of holes:	18
Length:	6800 yards
Par:	71
Visitors:	Visitors welcome
Requirements:	None
Handicap Limits:	None
Restrictions:	All visitors are welcome at any time, but it is wise to pre-book by telephone, especially at weekends
Parties:	Contact Sidon Ruddy or Gerard Ruddy on 0404 47415
Green fees:	IR£25 per round weekdays, IR£30 weekends. 10% reduction for groups of 20 or more.
Hire facilities:	⊤
Practice ground:	Large practice areas
Catering:	Restaurant with full menu

The European Golf Club: view

The European Golf Club: view

GREYSTONES GOLF CLUB
(ESTABLISHED 1895)
Greystones, Co. Wicklow

The club is situated in the north of County Wicklow about 20 miles from Dublin. It has a varied and scenic layout, the first nine holes being fairly flat, but the back nine much more hilly. There are spectacular views of the Wicklow coast and on a clear day the Welsh mountains can be seen from the 17th.

Secretary:	Oliver Walsh Tel 01 2874136 Fax 01 2873749
Professional:	Kevin Dacy Tel 01 28753081
Type:	Parkland
No of holes:	18
Length:	5401 metres
Par:	68
Visitors:	Visitors welcome
Requirements:	H M
Handicap Limits:	None
Restrictions:	Visitors restricted on Monday, Tuesday and Friday. Wednesdays with member only before 6.00pm.
Parties:	Please contact Oliver Walsh
Green fees:	IR£20 per round
Hire facilities:	C T Ca
Practice ground:	None
Catering:	Catering facilities Wednesday – Sunday in winter; seven days a week in summer

KILCOOLE
Kilcoole, Co. Wicklow

A nine-hole parkland course which is playable twelve months of the year. It features Ireland's only island green to date, the par 3 3rd hole, as well as the fifth longest hole in the country - the par 5 8th at 600 yards. The terrain is quite level and in a scenically beautiful setting under the gaze of the Sugar Loaf mountain, only a quarter of a mile from the Irish Sea.

Secretary:	Pat McEntaggart Tel 01 2872066
Professional:	None
Type:	Parkland
No of holes:	9
Length:	2753 metres
Par:	35
Visitors:	Visitors welcome
Requirements:	None
Handicap Limits:	Gentlemen 28; Ladies 36; Juniors 25
Restrictions:	No visitors on Saturday and Sunday
Parties:	Please contact the Secretary
Green fees:	IR£10 per round
Hire facilities:	**B**
Practice ground:	Putting green and practice ground
Catering:	New clubhouse under construction. Snacks available in temporary clubhouse. Parties catered for at local hotel.

OLD CONNA GOLF CLUB
(ESTABLISHED 1987)
Ferndale Road, Bray, Co. Wicklow

Eighteen-hole parkland course in scenic setting.

Secretary:	Dave Diviney, Secretary/Manager
	Tel 01 2826055 Fax 01 2825611
Professional:	Niall Murray Tel 01 2820822
Type:	Parkland
No of holes:	18
Length:	6550 yards
Par:	72
Visitors:	Visitors welcome
Requirements:	None
Handicap Limits:	None
Restrictions:	Visitors Monday to Friday only. Ladies Day is Tuesday. Best days for visitors are Mondays, Thursdays and Fridays.
Parties:	Parties welcome. Contact Secretary/Manager
Green fees:	IR£20 per round. No special rates.
Hire facilities:	**C** **T**
Practice ground:	Practice fairway and green. Putting green.
Catering:	Full catering facilities available

RATHSALLAGH GOLF CLUB
(ESTABLISHED 1994)
Nr. Dunlavin, Co. Wicklow

Rathsallagh was designed by former World Amateur Champion and
England Captain Peter McEvoy and Christy O'Connor Jnr. The course, on
250 acres of mature parkland, was built to USGA specifications making
the best use of the natural landscape. A mere 32 miles from Dublin, the
course promises to be one of the most exciting developments in the British
Isles.

Secretary:	David O'Flynn Tel 045 53112
	Fax 045 53343
Professional:	None
Type:	Parkland
No of holes:	18
Length:	6956 yards
Par:	72
Visitors:	Visitors welcome
Requirements:	None
Handicap Limits:	None
Restrictions:	Weekends dawn - 10.30am and 1.00 - 2.30pm.
	Weekends: Juniors over 16 years only.
Parties:	Contact David O'Flynn on 045 53112
Green fees:	IR£30 per round or per day. Special rates contact
	David O'Flynn.
Hire facilities:	C T
Practice ground:	Practice green, tees and bunkers
Catering:	Full bar and restaurant

Rathsallagh Golf Club

WICKLOW GOLF CLUB

(ESTABLISHED 1904)

Dunbur Road, Wicklow, Co. Wicklow

1904

The recently extended (1994) eighteen-hole course is situated along the cliffs overlooking Wicklow Bay on the outskirts of Wicklow town. It has panoramic views from every point on the course with the Wicklow Hills to the west and the Irish Sea to the east. With the introduction of eleven new holes the course provides a true test of golf for all abilities. Every hole has its own distinctive feature. The par 3s will test even the most accurate of golfers, with the 17th in particular – from an elevated tee over two 'watery graves' - a sight to behold.

Secretary:	Joe Kelly, Hon. Secretary Tel 0404 67379
Professional:	David Daly Tel 0404 66122
Type:	Parkland
No of holes:	18
Length:	6260 yards (5695 metres)
Par:	71
Visitors:	Visitors welcome
Requirements:	None
Handicap Limits:	Gentlemen 28; Ladies 36; Juniors 0
Restrictions:	Restricted only on Sundays - all day
Parties:	Please contact Hon. Secretary. Reduced green fee for parties over 20.
Green fees:	IR£15 per round; IR£12 for groups over 20
Hire facilities:	None
Practice ground:	Practice facilities available
Catering:	Bar snacks, lunch and dinner

WOODBROOK GOLF CLUB
(ESTABLISHED 1926)
Dublin Road, Bray, Co. Wicklow

The club was affiliated to the GUI in 1926 after a long association with cricket, and the rail track which crosses the course was laid down for the convenience of cricket spectators! The course is a seaside parkland layout and is maintained to a high level at all times - it is very popular with visiting groups and societies. There are wonderful views from Killiney Head to Bray Head and the 18th hole, with the railway track on the right, makes a very testing finish. The course is located eleven miles south of Dublin city on the N11.

Secretary:	Derek Smyth Tel 01 2824799 Fax 01 2821950
Professional:	Billy Kinsella Tel 01 2824799
Type:	Parkland
No of holes:	18
Length:	5966 metres
Par:	72
Visitors:	Visitors welcome
Requirements:	H M
Handicap Limits:	None
Restrictions:	Visitors restricted on Tuesdays, weekends and public holidays. Please telephone to make a prior appointment.
Parties:	Contact Secretary
Green fees:	IR£25 Monday to Friday, IR£35 weekends and public holidays
Hire facilities:	C T Ca
Practice ground:	None
Catering:	Full restaurant facilities in clubhouse

WOODENBRIDGE GOLF CLUB

(ESTABLISHED 1884)

Vale of Avoca, Arklow, Co. Wicklow

Woodenbridge is one of the oldest clubs in Ireland, established in 1884 as a nine-hole course. Set in the beautiful Vale of Avoca, it is surrounded by high woodlands and guarded by the River Avoca. The course has now been extended to a full eighteen holes and is in great demand since it opened up for play in July 1994. Great praise is due to its architect, Mr Paddy Merrigan, for a wonderful creation.

Secretary:	Henry Crummy, Hon. Sec. Tel 0402 35202
	Fax 0402 31460
Professional:	None
Type:	Parkland
No of holes:	18
Length:	6316 yards
Par:	71
Visitors:	Visitors welcome
Requirements:	None
Handicap Limits:	None
Restrictions:	No visitors at all on Thursdays and Saturdays
Parties:	Contact Henry Crummy, Hon. Sec.
Green fees:	IR£20 per round. Special rates only if playing with member.
Hire facilities:	T
Practice ground:	Practice ground available to visitors
Catering:	Excellent dining facilities and cuisine

MUNSTER GOLF CLUBS

Co. Clare
Dromoland
 Castle
Ennis
Kilkee
Lahinch
Shannon
Spanish Point

Co. Cork
Bandon
Bantry Park
Berehaven Park
Charleville
Cobh
Cork

Douglas
East Cork
Fota Island
Glengarriff
Harbour Point
Kinsale
Lee Valley
Mahon
Mallow
Monkstown
Muskerry
Skibbereen
Youghal

Co. Kerry
Ballybunion
Beaufort

Ceann Sibeal
 (Dingle)
Dooks
Kenmare
Killarney
Killorglin
Parknasilla
Tralee
Waterville

Co. Limerick
Adare Manor
Castletroy
Limerick

Co. Tipperary
Ballykisteen
Clonmel
County Tipperary
Nenagh
Roscrea
Thurles

Co. Waterford
Dunmore East
Faithlegg
Lismore
Tramore
Waterford
Waterford
 Castle
West Waterford

DROMOLAND CASTLE GOLF CLUB
(ESTABLISHED 1961)
Newmarket-on-Fergus, Co. Clare

This is a championship course set in rich woodland around a natural lake and has extensive views of a beautifully restored castle, now a luxury hotel. The later holes boast expansive landscape views of the River Shannon along with the neighbouring counties of Limerick and Kerry. Other holes are complemented by the River Rine which gently flows through the estate. Scenically beautiful, with lots of wildlife to be seen, in recent years Dromoland has been the home of the Whyte & MacKay Pro-Celebrity Golf Tournament and the course has been played by many noted players.

Secretary:	Mr J. O'Halloran Tel 061 363355
Professional:	Philip Murphy Tel 061 368444
Type:	Parkland
No of holes:	18
Length:	6098 yards
Par:	71
Visitors:	Visitors welcome
Requirements:	H
Handicap Limits:	Gentlemen 28; Ladies 36; Juniors: 24
Restrictions:	None
Parties:	Contact Secretary/Manager
Green fees:	Weekday IR£20, IR£25 weekends
Hire facilities:	C T Ca Pc B
Practice ground:	Large area with two practice greens
Catering:	Facilities available

Score card details

Hole	1	2	3	4	5	6	7	8	9	10	11	12	13	14	15	16	17	18
Yds	353	472	209	419	374	509	127	354	198	264	437	314	106	354	254	344	149	409
Par	4	5	3	4	4	5	3	4	3	4	5	4	3	4	4	4	3	5

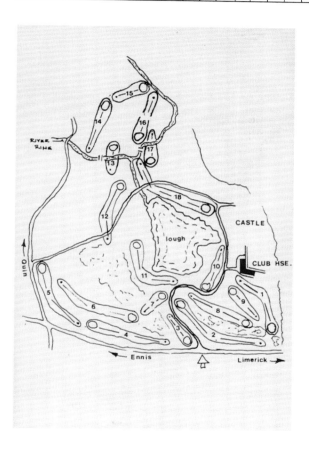

Dromoland Golf Club: course plan

Dromoland Castle Golf Club

ENNIS GOLF CLUB
(ESTABLISHED 1907)
Drumbiggle Road, Ennis, Co. Clare

The town of Ennis is ideally situated to serve as your gateway to the West of Ireland. Just 15 miles from Shannon Airport and on the primary road to the West of Ireland, Ennis is very well served by top class hotels, and is less than one mile from the town centre. The club is noted for its hospitality.

Secretary:	Maurice Walshe Tel 065 24074 Fax 065 41848
Professional:	Martin Ward Tel 065 20690
Type:	Parkland
No of holes:	18
Length:	5316 metres
Par:	69
Visitors:	Visitors welcome
Requirements:	**M**
Handicap Limits:	None
Restrictions:	No visitors Tuesday afternoons, Wednesday mornings or Sundays
Parties:	Please contact Club Secretary
Green fees:	IR£15 per day. Group rates available on request.
Hire facilities:	**C** **T** **Ca**
Practice ground:	Practice area available
Catering:	Snacks and full meals available daily in the clubhouse until 10.00pm

KILKEE GOLF CLUB
(ESTABLISHED 1896)
East End, Kilkee, Co. Clare

This new championship standard course has some dramatic holes overlooking the Atlantic Ocean. The clubhouse overlooks Kilkee Bay and the restaurant and bar have scenic views of the sailing, diving and other watersports in the Bay. There is a well-stocked golf shop and the clubhouse is only ten minutes' walk from the centre of Kilkee with its selection of hotels, apartments, hostels and guest houses. Kilkee is a one-hour drive from Shannon Airport and enjoys a relaxed holiday night-life with a choice of restaurants, bars and musical entertainment, as well as very enjoyable golf.

Secretary:	Thomas Lillis. Business Manager John Williams Tel 065 56048
Professional:	None
Type:	Links/clifftop
No of holes:	18
Length:	5900 metres
Par:	72
Visitors:	Visitors welcome
Requirements:	None
Handicap Limits:	None
Restrictions:	No restrictions for gentlemen and ladies. Juniors permitted before 10.00am or between 4.00 and 6.00pm.
Parties:	Contact Business Manager, John Williams
Green fees:	IR£15 per round. Group rates on application.
Hire facilities:	C T Ca B
Practice ground:	Practice ground available
Catering:	Full bar and restaurant from 10.00am to 10.00pm every day

LAHINCH GOLF CLUB
(ESTABLISHED 1892)
Lahinch, Co. Clare

Officers of the Black Watch and some local enthusiasts founded Lahinch
Golf Club on Good Friday 1893. The original course was designed by
'Old' Tom Morris, but was extensively revised in 1928 by Dr Alastair
MacKenzie, who also designed Pebble Beach, Cypress Point and Augusta
National. The Castle course was added in 1975. At Lahinch everybody is a
golf enthusiast and this quickly transmits itself to the visitor – hence it is
known as the St Andrews of Irish golf. A feature of Lahinch is the goats
that graze on the dunes, but seek shelter by the clubhouse when rain
approaches.

Secretary:	Alan Reardon Tel 065 81003 Fax 065 81592	
Professional:	Robert McCavery Tel 065 81003	
	Course 1: Old	**Course 2:** Castle
Type:	Links	Links
No of holes:	18	18
Length:	6123 metres	5138 metres
Par:	72	70

Visitors:	Visitors welcome
Requirements:	H M
Handicap Limits:	Gentlemen 28; Ladies 36; Juniors 36
Restrictions:	No restrictions
Parties:	Please contact Alan Reardon. Note that IR£25 deposit is required on confirmation of booking.
Green fees:	Old Course IR£30 per round. Castle Course IR£18 per round. Day booking for both courses IR£40.
Hire facilities:	C T Ca B
Practice ground:	Practice ground and putting green
Catering:	Full bar and restaurant facilities are available.

Lahinch Golf Club

Score card details: Old Course

Hole	1	2	3	4	5	6	7	8	9	10	11	12	13	14	15	16	17	18
Yds	352	468	138	391	441	142	365	320	351	412	126	434	250	446	422	178	400	487
Par	4	5	3	4	5	3	4	4	4	4	3	4	4	5	4	3	4	5

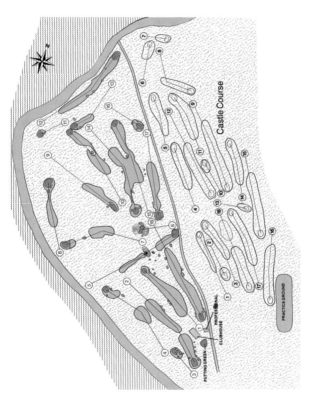

Lahinch Golf Club: course plan (Old Course)

SHANNON GOLF CLUB
(ESTABLISHED 1966)
Shannon Airport, Co. Clare

Shannon Golf Club is located 500 yards beyond the Airport Terminal
Building. It was designed by John D. Harris, a noted golf architect.
Ballesteros, Norman, Faldo, Lyle, Langer, and O'Connor Jnr have all rated
this parkland championship course highly. It is bordered by the River
Shannon with some magnificent views of the Shannon Estuary. Water is a
feature on a number of holes, in particular at the 17th par 3 of 216 yards.
Trees, which are strategically placed along the beautifully manicured
fairways, put a premium on accuracy.

Secretary:	Donough J. Lempriere, Secretary/Manager Tel 061 471849 Fax 061 471507
Professional:	Artie Pyke Tel 061 471551
Type:	Parkland
No of holes:	18
Length:	6874 yards (6186 metres)
Par:	72
Visitors:	Visitors welcome
Requirements:	H M
Handicap Limits:	Gentlemen 28; Ladies 36; Juniors 28
Restrictions:	Tuesday is Ladies Day. Limited tee availability on Sundays for Ladies and Gentlemen. Juniors must be accompanied by an adult.
Parties:	Please contact Secretary/Manager to make prior booking
Green fees:	IR£20 per round weekdays, IR£25 weekends. Large groups/societies 10% discount.
Hire facilities:	C T Ca B
Practice ground:	Large practice ground adjoining car park
Catering:	Catering 11.00am - 9.00pm Monday to Sunday. Full *à la carte* menu.

SPANISH POINT GOLF CLUB
Spanish Point, Milltown Malbay, Co. Clare

A challenging nine-hole links course overlooking the beach at Spanish Point. Strong winds from the Atlantic come very much into play and make the six par 3s difficult to club. The course is playable all the year round. Spanish Point is located two miles from Milltown Malbay.

Secretary:	Gerry O'Loughran Tel 065 84198/84334
Professional:	None
Type:	Links
No of holes:	9
Length:	1787 yards
Par:	30
Visitors:	Visitors welcome
Requirements:	H (for open competitions only)
Handicap Limits:	None
Restrictions:	Visitors restricted on Sundays. Juniors under 14 not allowed after 5.00pm or on Saturday or Sunday.
Parties:	Please contact Secretary in advance
Green fees:	IR£10 per round, IR£5 with member.
Hire facilities:	Please check with Secretary
Practice ground:	None
Catering:	Sandwiches and light snacks available

BANDON GOLF CLUB
(ESTABLISHED 1909)
Castlebernard, Bandon, Co. Cork

This well-established eighteen-hole course is renowned for its scenic
setting in the beautiful valley of Bandon, and represents a true test of your
golfing skills. The 200-year-old trees on the 2nd and 3rd holes should be
regarded as wonderful creations of nature - not as obstructions. Bandon
was the first club in West Cork to extend to eighteen-holes (1978). Shrewd
management and a vigorous planting programme means that the course
now has many mature groves and spinneys. The clubhouse was extended
in 1988 and now offers a wide range of facilities to visitors.

Secretary:	Barry O'Neill Tel 023 41111 Fax 023 44690
Professional:	Paddy O'Boyle Tel 023 42224
Type:	Parkland
No of holes:	18
Length:	5663 metres
Par:	70
Visitors:	Visitors welcome
Requirements:	None
Handicap Limits:	None
Restrictions:	None
Parties:	Contact Hon. Secretary
Green fees:	IR£12 per day weekdays. IR£15 weekends and public holidays.

Hire facilities: C   T   B

Practice ground:	No
Catering:	Full bar and dining facilities

BANTRY PARK GOLF CLUB
(ESTABLISHED 1975)
Donemark, Bantry, Co. Cork

Very attractive nine-hole course. Opening hole is an interesting par 3.

Secretary:	Michael Milner Tel 027 50372
Professional:	None
Type:	Parkland
No of holes:	9
Length:	2973 yards
Par:	36
Visitors:	Visitors welcome
Requirements:	None
Handicap Limits:	None
Restrictions:	None
Parties:	Write to Jerry Sheehan, Ardnagaoithe, Bantry, Co. Cork
Green fees:	IR£10 per day
Hire facilities:	C Ca T B
Practice ground:	Practice ground available
Catering:	Bar and pub grub - sausages, chips, sandwiches, etc.

BEREHAVEN PARK GOLF CLUB
(ESTABLISHED 1987)
Millcove, Berehaven, Co. Cork

Berehaven Park Golf Club is approximately 80 miles from Cork City. It is a nine-hole course set in beautiful surroundings in the Beara Peninsula in West Cork. The facilities are plentiful in the adjacent Amenity Park which incorporates the golf club. There is a deep-water pier suitable for berthing yachts, a camper van service area, camping sites and a safe bathing beach – sailing and surfing are very popular sports. The club welcomes visitors and societies and the course is popular and playable all year. Family membership IR£45, individual membership IR£95 and country members IR£60.

Secretary:	Mr J. J. McLaughlin Tel 027 70039
Professional:	None
Type:	Seaside links
No of holes:	9 (played from outward and inward tees)
Length:	4763 metres
Par:	68
Visitors:	Visitors welcome
Requirements:	**H** **M**
Handicap Limits:	Gentlemen 28; Ladies 36; Juniors 36
Restrictions:	Tee times available every day - prior arrangements to be made with Secretary or Club Captain. Ring 027 70700 for details from 10.30am.
Parties:	Please contact 027 70700
Green fees:	IR£8 per round Monday to Friday, IR£10 weekends.
Hire facilities:	**C** **T** **Ca** **B**
Practice ground:	Limited practice ground
Catering:	Full catering and dining facilities in Pavilion; also games room, sauna and gymnasium. Camper and camping accomodation.

CHARLEVILLE GOLF CLUB
(ESTABLISHED 1941)
Charleville, Co. Cork

This is a well-known and popular parkland course with numerous trees. It is situated on the main road from Cork to Limerick. Visitors are welcome but should always contact the club before coming. The course has two par 5s, three par 3s and thirteen par 4s. From July/August 1995 a new nine holes designed by G.T.I., Stirling, Scotland should be in play with extensive practice areas, driving range, etc.

Secretary:	James A. Murphy, Hon. Sec. Tel 063 81257 Fax 063 81274
Professional:	None
Type:	Parkland
No of holes:	18
Length:	6430 yards
Par:	71
Visitors:	Visitors welcome
Requirements:	None
Handicap Limits:	None
Restrictions:	Visitors restricted on Saturdays and Sundays and other times when competitions are arranged. Most other times freely available. Always contact club by telephone before coming.
Parties:	Contact Secretary or Manager, Matt Keane.
Green fees:	IR£12 per round weekdays. IR£15 weekends. No special rates for Societies and groups.
Hire facilities:	🅣 🅑
Practice ground:	Practice ground available. Driving range planned for 1995.
Catering:	Full meals and snacks

COBH GOLF CLUB
(ESTABLISHED 1987)
Ballywilliam, Cobh, Co. Cork

The Cobh course is situated two miles east of Cobh town. The well-known architect Eddie Hackett designed the course, which was opened on 19th September 1987 by Christy O'Connor Snr. The main feature of the course is the 7th par 3 hole which has out of bounds all down the right-hand side and behind the green. Course record: Professional 64, Amateur 62.

Secretary:	Mr D. A. Kilcullen Tel 021 811536
Professional:	None
Type:	Parkland
No of holes:	9
Length:	2518 yards
Par:	33
Visitors:	Visitors welcome
Requirements:	None
Handicap Limits:	Gentlemen none; Ladies none; Juniors 18
Restrictions:	Visitors play restricted at weekends. All Juniors must play with an adult.
Parties:	Please contact Henry Cunningham on 021 812399
Green fees:	IR£9 per round. Special rates for Societies.
Hire facilities:	C
Practice ground:	Putting and pitching greens, and bunkers
Catering:	Snacks only at present - new clubhouse being built

CORK GOLF CLUB
(ESTABLISHED 1888)
Little Island, Cork, Co. Cork

Established in 1888 and redesigned in 1927 by the world-famous golf architect Alister Mackenzie, this championship parkland course is as graceful and mature as its age would suggest. Scenically situated in Cork Harbour, the club has played host to major amateur and professional championships over the years, including the Carrolls Irish Open, the Irish Professional and Irish Close Championships and the National Finals. The variety and complexity of the course attracts top-class golfers, while the forward tees will test and delight the competent player.

Secretary:	Matt Sands Tel 021 353451 Fax 021 353410
Professional:	Ted Higgins Tel 021 353421
Type:	Parkland
No of holes:	18
Length:	6115 metres
Par:	72
Visitors:	Visitors welcome
Requirements:	**H**
Handicap Limits:	Gentlemen 28; Ladies 36; Juniors 36
Restrictions:	Monday, Tuesday, Wednesday and Friday except 12.30 - 2.00pm or after 4.00pm. Thursday, Saturday and Sunday after 2.30pm.
Parties:	Please contact Secretary
Green fees:	IR£23 midweek; IR£26 weekend, per round and per day
Hire facilities:	**T** **B**
Practice ground:	Yes
Catering:	Yes

Cork Golf Club

Score card details

Hole	1	2	3	4	5	6	7	8	9	10	11	12	13	14	15	16	17	18
Yds	340	460	244	411	510	300	169	379	178	374	454	289	157	397	383	323	360	387
Par	4	5	4	4	5	4	3	4	3	4	5	4	3	4	4	4	4	4

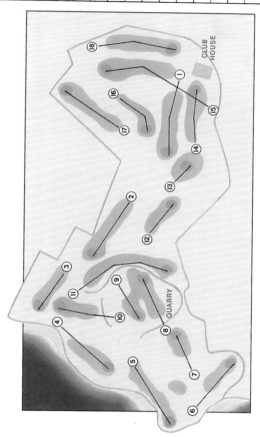

Cork Golf Club: course plan

DOUGLAS GOLF CLUB
(ESTABLISHED 1910)
Douglas, Co. Cork

Douglas Golf Club is situated on an elevated site about three miles from
Cork City, and covers 109 acres. The views from the clubhouse are
breathtaking and must be regarded as some of the most panoramic in the
country. Landmarks in Cork City can be easily seen, as can the
Knockmealdown Mountains, over 30 miles away. The club has a
distinguished history of producing notable players, both ladies and
gentlemen, and the winning of the Barton Shield in 1991 brought great
pride and satisfaction to Douglas.

Secretary:	Brian Barrett, Secretary/Manager
	Tel 021 895297
Professional:	Garry Nicholson Tel 021 362055
Type:	Parkland
No of holes:	18
Length:	5664 metres
Par:	70
Visitors:	Visitors welcome
Requirements:	None
Handicap Limits:	None
Restrictions:	All visitors restricted on Saturday and Sunday mornings and on Tuesdays up to 6.00pm. It is essential to ring in advance to confirm availability.
Parties:	Contact Brian Barrett, Manager. Advance booking essential. Bookings made in January each year.
Green fees:	IR£18 per round, IR£27 per day. No special rates.
Hire facilities:	Ⓒ Ⓣ
Practice ground:	None
Catering:	Bar food availalbe to 6.00pm. Full dining facilities available from noon to 10.00pm.

Score card details

Hole	1	2	3	4	5	6	7	8	9	10	11	12	13	14	15	16	17	18
Yds	243	341	409	140	393	346	170	443	297	307	351	364	341	382	140	370	242	385
Par	4	4	4	3	4	4	3	5	4	4	4	4	4	4	3	4	4	4

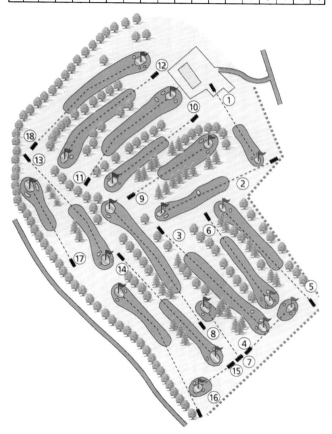

Douglas Golf Club: course plan

EAST CORK GOLF CLUB
(ESTABLISHED 1970)
Gortacrue, Midleton, Co. Cork

The club was founded in 1968 when Eamonn Moloney decided to evict his prize dairy herd and convert his farm into a golf course. He enlisted the aid of Eddie Hackett, one of Ireland's foremost golf architects, to carry out the design and Ned Moran, a local site-development contractor, to build the course. The original nine-hole course was opened in November 1969. Extension to eighteen holes was completed in 1975. The course has now matured into one of the most attractive and challenging parklands in the country; new members and visitors are always made welcome.

Secretary:	David Coleman Tel 021 632819 (home)
	Tel. 021 631687 (club)
Professional:	None
Type:	Parkland
No of holes:	18
Length:	5207 metres
Par:	69
Visitors:	Visitors welcome
Requirements:	**H** **M** (for open competitions)
Handicap Limits:	Gentlemen 28; Ladies 36; Juniors 36
Restrictions:	Monday is Ladies Day. Saturday and Sunday: members' competitions most weekends. In summer, Tuesday evenings mixed foursomes.
Parties:	Contact Miss Joan Ahern at the Club (021 631687)
Green fees:	IR£12 per day. Special rates: enquire by telephone or letter.
Hire facilities:	**T**
Practice ground:	Putting green
Catering:	Bar menu available

FOTA ISLAND GOLF CLUB

(ESTABLISHED 1993)

Carrigtwohill, Co. Cork

Fota Island sits tranquilly in Cork Harbour, a few minutes' drive from Cork with its international airport and car ferry terminal. Fota is very much a traditional golf course, featuring clusters of pot bunkers, a double green and challenging undulating putting surfaces. The course is maintained to the highest standards to ensure year-round golfing enjoyment. The clubhouse incorporates the creative conversion of some beautiful stone farm buildings with ground-level spike bar. 'Niblicks' restaurant overlooks the 18th green.

Secretary:	Kevin Mulcahy Tel 021 883700 Fax 021 883713
Professional:	Kevin Morris Tel 021 883710
Type:	Parkland
No of holes:	18
Length:	6891 yards (6355 metres)
Par:	72
Visitors:	Visitors welcome
Requirements:	None
Handicap Limits:	None
Restrictions:	All visitors: members time 12.30 - 2.30pm every day and 9.30 - 10.30 weekends. Ladies: members time 9.00 - 11.00am every day and 1.00 - 2.00pm Tuesdays.
Parties:	Please contact the Professional's Shop: discounts for groups of over 20.
Green fees:	IR£27 per round weekdays, IR£30 weekends. Extra round IR£10.
Hire facilities:	C T Ca Pc (from 1995) B
Practice ground:	Driving range with grass teeing area
Catering:	Snack food in bar. Full service dining room. Also private dining/meeting room.

Fota Island Golf Club

Score card details

Hole	1	2	3	4	5	6	7	8	9	10	11	12	13	14	15	16	17	18
Yds	428	435	182	501	577	375	170	484	425	502	201	425	183	440	445	417	204	492
Par	4	4	3	5	5	4	3	5	4	5	3	4	3	4	4	4	3	5

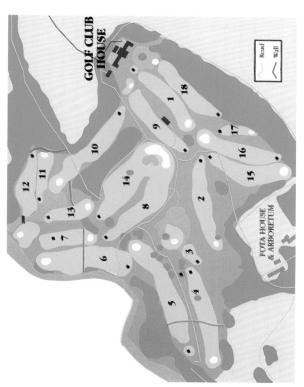

Fota Island Golf Club: course plan

GLENGARRIFF GOLF CLUB
(ESTABLISHED 1935)
Glengarriff, Co. Cork

One mile from Glengarriff village, overlooking the harbour and the Coha Mountain range with Garnish Island in the background.

Secretary:	John Brooks Tel 027 63134
Professional:	None
Type:	Links
No of holes:	9
Length:	2047 metres
Par:	33
Visitors:	Visitors welcome
Requirements:	None
Handicap Limits:	None
Restrictions:	No restrictions for visitors
Parties:	Contact Secretary
Green fees:	IR£10 per day

Hire facilities: C   T   B

Practice ground:	None
Catering:	Tea, coffee and sandwiches available

HARBOUR POINT GOLF CLUB
(ESTABLISHED 1991)
Clash, Little Island, Co. Cork

Overlooking Cork's sweeping landscape, Harbour Point is now well established as a premier championship course. This in itself is a deserved tribute to its widespread appeal, given that the course was only opened for play in June 1991. In its layout and design, it represents a test for the best. Harbour Point provides for a full range of shot-making, from the demands of the par 3s to the precision required for the rest of the tree-lined holes. The course is less than six miles from Cork city centre and within a short drive of the airport and ferryport.

Secretary:	Niamh O'Connell Tel 021 353094
Professional:	None resident, but lessons available Shop 021 353719.
Type:	Parkland
No of holes:	18
Length:	White 5773 metres
Par:	72
Visitors:	Visitors welcome
Requirements:	None
Handicap Limits:	None
Restrictions:	None
Parties:	Special rates for groups of 20 or more. Please contact Secretary.
Green fees:	IR£20 per round and per day, but IR£10 before 11.00am on Monday, Wednesday, Thursday and Friday.
Hire facilities:	C B
Practice ground:	21-bay, all-weather floodlit driving range
Catering:	Full bar and restaurant with extensive menu

Harbour Point Golf Club

KINSALE GOLF CLUB
(ESTABLISHED 1912)
Ringenane, Belgooly, Kinsale, Co. Cork

The new course is situated in a tranquil rural setting in the lush rolling terrain of the Bandon Valley. It is close to the town of Kinsale, eight miles from Cork Airport and twelve miles from the city centre. The old Bandon railway track runs alongside the course and the tiny Farrangalway railway station, although out of use since 1933, is located by the entrance to the new course. The gentle rolling landscape is ideally suited to the development of a golf course and the exceptionally dry nature of the soil guarantees all-year-round golf. New course opens in summer 1995.

Secretary:	Mr J. J. Murphy Tel 021 772197	
Professional:	None	

	Course 1: Ringenane	**Course 2:** Farrangalway (under construction)
Type:	Parkland	Parkland
No of holes:	9	18
Length:	2666 metres	6500 yards
Par:	35	71

Visitors:	Visitors welcome
Requirements:	**M**
Handicap Limits:	None
Restrictions:	No visitors Saturdays and Sundays. Weekdays reserved for members after 4.00pm.
Parties:	Please contact the Secretary
Green fees:	IR£12 per day. IR£8 for societies.
Hire facilities:	**C** **T**
Practice ground:	Practice ground when new course opens
Catering:	Bar food available seven days a week

LEE VALLEY GOLF & COUNTRY CLUB
(ESTABLISHED 1993)
Clashanure, Ovens, Co. Cork

Designed by Christy O'Connor Jnr and situated only eight miles from
Cork City, this outstanding eighteen-hole championship golf course offers
all golf enthusiasts a very relaxed yet challenging game of golf. Set in the
Lee Valley on the main Cork/Killarney Road (N22), it has scenic views of
the Lee Valley and the Cork and Kerry Mountains. Seven of the eighteen
holes have water as a major hazard, and this along with the undulating
terrain provides a stern test of your golfing abilities. The course also has
the unique feature of two historic 'Fairy Forts' over 300 years old.

Secretary:	Barry O'Connell Tel 021 331721
	Fax 021 331695
Professional:	Brendan McDaid
Type:	Parkland
No of holes:	18
Length:	6705 yards
Par:	72
Visitors:	Visitors welcome
Requirements:	H
Handicap Limits:	Gentlemen 28; Ladies 36; Juniors 36
Restrictions:	Visitors restricted during members' times between 1.00 - 2.00pm Monday to Friday and from dawn to 11.15am and 1.15 - 2.30pm Saturdays, Sundays and public holidays.
Parties:	Contact Barry O'Connell or Kathleen Bond
Green fees:	Green fees not quoted
Hire facilities:	C T Ca B
Practice ground:	Indoor driving range and outdoor practice area
Catering:	Bar and restaurant (both also open to the public)

Lee Valley Golf Club

MAHON GOLF CLUB
(ESTABLISHED 1980)
Skehard Road, Blackrock, Co. Cork

Nine-hole public course built on attractive location by river bank.

Secretary:	Tim O'Connor, Secretary/Manager
	Tel 021 294280
Professional:	None
Type:	Parkland
No of holes:	18
Length:	4818 metres
Par:	68
Visitors:	Visitors welcome
Requirements:	None
Handicap Limits:	None
Restrictions:	No visitors 7.30 - 11.30am Saturday and Sunday
Parties:	Please contact Tim O'Connor. Parties and societies welcome.
Green fees:	IR£8.50 per round Monday to Friday, IR£9.50 Saturday and Sunday. Special party rates can be arranged.
Hire facilities:	⃞C ⃞T ⃞Ca
Practice ground:	No practice ground
Catering:	Full catering facilities

MALLOW GOLF CLUB

Ballyellis, Mallow, Co. Cork

A championship course of eighteen holes, 21 miles north of Cork city. No details can be supplied regarding the course until the present reconstruction is complete.

Secretary:	Michael O'Sullivan Tel 022 22591
Professional:	Sean Conway Tel 022 21145
Type:	Parkland
No of holes:	18
Length:	To be confirmed
Par:	70
Visitors:	

At the time of going to press the construction of the clubhouse and the facilities available on the course have been undergoing extensive reconstruction: no details therefore available.

MONKSTOWN GOLF CLUB
(ESTABLISHED 1908)
Parkgarriffe, Monkstown, Co. Cork

A testing, mature parkland layout, recently enhanced by the introduction of 83 tough new bunkers. Some notable water features at the 10th, 15th and 16th holes, where bravery reaps rewards. Particularly good greens, kept receptive by the judicious use of the automatic watering system. A major clubhouse extension was completed in spring 1994.

Secretary:	Mr E. A. Finn, Manager Tel 021 841376
Professional:	Batt Murphy Tel 021 841686
Type:	Parkland
No of holes:	18
Length:	5669 metres
Par:	70
Visitors:	Visitors welcome
Requirements:	H M
Handicap Limits:	Gentlemen 20; Ladies 30; Juniors 14
Restrictions:	No visitors between 1.00 - 2.00pm or after 4.00pm weekdays or between 8.00 - 11.00am and 12.00 - 2.00pm weekends. Restrictions also when major competitions or societies visiting.
Parties:	Please contact Manager - essential to book well in advance
Green fees:	IR£20 per round, but Friday, Saturday and Sunday IR£23. Special rates for societies over 24 players.
Hire facilities:	C T
Practice ground:	Putting green and large practice ground
Catering:	Bar and dining room available

MUSKERRY GOLF CLUB

(ESTABLISHED 1897)

Carrigrohane, Co. Cork

The first five holes are on flat terrain. The 6th hole (par 3) is across river to ledges of hill crest. 7th to 14th holes spiral around and up hill - interesting and hugely scenic. The 15th hole (par 3) is difficult to club depending on wind direction. 16th, 17th and 18th holes are played across and with the course of the river - very demanding finishing holes. Anyone achieving par of 3, 4, 4 and 4 is playing excellent golf.

Secretary:	Mr J. J. Moynihan Tel 021 385297
Professional:	M. Lehane Tel 021 381445
Type:	Parkland
No of holes:	18
Length:	5426 metres
Par:	71
Visitors:	Visitors welcome
Requirements:	H
Handicap Limits:	None
Restrictions:	All visitors restricted Monday and Tuesday all day, Wednesday up to 11.30am, Thursday after 12.30pm, Friday up to 4.00pm, Saturday and Sunday after 3.00pm.
Parties:	Please contact Secretary
Green fees:	IR£12 per round, IR£15 per day. Societies IR£13.
Hire facilities:	C B
Practice ground:	No
Catering:	Bar snacks, salads and full meals available. It would be helpful if full meals are ordered before commencing play.

SKIBBEREEN GOLF CLUB
(ESTABLISHED 1931)
Licknavar, Skibbereen, Co. Cork

In 1993 Skibbereen Golf Club was extended from nine to eighteen holes and has a good mix of tricky short holes and interesting longer ones. There are some sand bunkers, and the greens are always in tip-top condition so that this links course is a must on your south-west tour.

Secretary:	Brenda O'Driscoll Tel 028 21227
Professional:	None
Type:	Parkland
No of holes:	18
Length:	5774 yards
Par:	68
Visitors:	Visitors welcome
Requirements:	None
Handicap Limits:	None
Restrictions:	Ladies Day Friday, tee reserved for two hours
Parties:	Contact Maeve O'Regan, P. R. O. at Club - negotiable
Green fees:	IR£12 per day but IR£15 July and August
Hire facilities:	T
Practice ground:	About 180 yards long with nine-hole putting green
Catering:	Bar food all day. Full meals in the evening.

YOUGHAL GOLF CLUB
(ESTABLISHED 1898)
Knockaverry, Youghal, Co. Cork

Youghal Golf Club was established before the turn of the century and for many years has hosted various Golfing Union inter-club championships. It is well maintained and is playable all year round. The course sits above the town, proudly overlooking a panoramic vista of beautiful sea views, with Capel Island guarding the south of the bay. Youghal town is situated on the N25, the main road from Rosslare, between Wateford and Cork City. Visitors from home and abroad are made welcome in the new clubhouse, which has a magnificent lounge bar.

Secretary:	Mr M. O'Sullivan Tel 024 92787 Fax 024 92461
Professional:	Liam Burns Tel 024 92590
Type:	Parkland
No of holes:	18
Length:	5664 metres
Par:	70
Visitors:	Visitors welcome
Requirements:	**M**
Handicap Limits:	Gentlemen 28; Ladies 36; Juniors 36
Restrictions:	Gentlemen and ladies any time except Wednesdays (Ladies day) but pre-booking available. Juniors after 5.00pm.
Parties:	Please contact M. O'Sullivan
Green fees:	IR£14 per day or per round. With member IR£7. Societies IR£12.
Hire facilities:	**C** **T**
Practice ground:	Practice net, putting green, small driving area
Catering:	Full catering facilities. Bar, restaurant.

BALLYBUNION GOLF CLUB
(ESTABLISHED 1894)
Links Road, Ballybunion, Co. Kerry

Golf on the Ballybunion links is an unforgettable golfing experience which should be savoured by all golfers, although it will be found to have extreme difficulty for those above 10 handicap. The Old Course is a great favourite of Tom Watson and Cashen is also much admired for its wonderful exploitation of the natural terrain.

Secretary:	Jim McKenna Tel 068 27146 Fax 068 27146
Professional:	Brian O'Callaghan Tel 068 27387

	Course 1: Old	**Course 2: Cashen**
Type:	Links	Links
No of holes:	18	18
Length:	6241 yards	5941 yards
Par:	71	71

Visitors:	Visitors welcome
Requirements:	H M
Handicap Limits:	Gentlemen 24; Ladies 36; Juniors 24
Restrictions:	All visitors book well in advance. Avoid weekends.
Parties:	Essential to contact office from 6.30am to 5.30pm (summertime)
Green fees:	Old IR£30, New IR£20 per round - IR£45 for both courses - July 18th - September 31st, Old IR£35, New IR£25, IR£50 per day for both courses.
Hire facilities:	C T Ca
Practice ground:	Practice fairway and putting green
Catering:	Lunch and dinner served from 12.30pm to 9.30pm

Score Card Details: Old Course

Hole	1	2	3	4	5	6	7	8	9	10	11	12	13	14	15	16	17	18
Yards	392	445	220	498	508	364	423	153	454	359	449	192	484	131	216	490	385	379
Par	4	4	3	5	5	4	4	3	4	4	4	3	5	3	3	5	4	4

Score Card Details: Cashen

Hole	1	2	3	4	5	6	7	8	9	10	11	12	13	14	15	16	17	18
Yards	324	146	237	395	400	487	199	479	368	432	377	154	350	378	155	314	605	478
Par	4	3	4	4	4	5	3	5	4	4	4	3	4	4	3	4	5	5

Ballybunion Golf Club

BEAUFORT GOLF COURSE
(ESTABLISHED 1994)
Churchtown, Beaufort, Killarney, Co. Kerry

Beaufort Golf Course is part of Churchtown Estate, the centrepiece of which is the Georgian house built in 1740 by Sir Roland Blennerhassett. The estate was bought in 1860 by James MacGillicuddy Magill, and it is his grandson and great grandsons who own it today, and who have developed this great course. The ruins of Castle Gore stand by the 13th green. The entrance to the course is lined with 200-year-old trees, and the pineapples which crown the gate pillars are a symbol of hospitality. The course presents great views of the world-famous MacGillicuddy Reeks from all points.

Secretary:	Colin Kelly Tel 064 44440 Fax 064 44752
Professional:	None
Type:	Parkland
No of holes:	18
Length:	6792 yards
Par:	71
Visitors:	Visitors welcome
Requirements:	None
Handicap Limits:	None
Restrictions:	The tee is reserved for members only on Saturdays and Sundays dawn - 9.30am and 1.30 - 2.30pm, Monday to Friday 1.30 - 2.30pm and every day after 5.30pm.
Parties:	Please contact Colin Kelly: minimum of 20 players
Green fees:	IR£20 per round weekdays, IR£25 weekends. Additional round IR£8 and IR£10 (if available).
Hire facilities:	C T Ca B
Practice ground:	Currently limited to five players. Large putting area.
Catering:	Tea, coffee, soup, sandwiches, salads. Full bar facilities.

CEANN SIBEAL (DINGLE) GOLF CLUB
(ESTABLISHED 1924)
Ballyferriter, Tralee, Co. Kerry

Ceann Sibeal is the most westerly golf course in Europe. It is set in the heart of Irish-speaking Ireland amidst breathtaking scenery. The club is renowned for hospitality and friendliness. The course is a links of the traditional Scottish variety - plenty of bunkers, strong winds and a winding 'burn'.

Secretary:	Mr G. Partington, Secretary/Manager
	Tel 066 56255/56408 Fax 066 56409
Professional:	None
Type:	Links
No of holes:	18
Length:	6650 yards
Par:	72
Visitors:	Visitors welcome
Requirements:	None
Handicap Limits:	None
Restrictions:	Avoid members' times. Always ring ahead.
Parties:	All welcome - contact Secretary/Manager
Green fees:	IR£18 per round. IR£23 per day. Special rates for large groups.
Hire facilities:	**C** **T** **Ca**
Practice ground:	Practice ground and putting green
Catering:	Bar/restaurant

DOOKS GOLF CLUB
(ESTABLISHED 1889)
Glenbeigh, Co. Kerry

Dooks is a testing eighteen-hole links course situated in one of the most picturesque corners of the Ring of Kerry. A breathtaking view of Dingle Bay and the McGillycuddy Reeks in the background make Dooks an idyllic golfing and holiday location. Considerable care has been given to the greens in recent years and, as a result, the popularity of Dooks as a true test of golf has grown and grown. A watering scheme to the greens was installed in 1972, the bar was extended in 1973, and the clubhouse completely renovated and enlarged in 1977/78. A gem worthy of a visit.

Secretary:	Michael Shanahan, Secretary/Manager Tel 066 68205 Fax 066 68476
Professional:	None
Type:	Links
No of holes:	18
Length:	6010 yards
Par:	70
Visitors:	Visitors welcome
Requirements:	H M
Handicap Limits:	Gentlemen 28; Ladies 36
Restrictions:	No restrictions
Parties:	Contact Secretary/Manager 066 68205
Green fees:	1994 prices IR£16 per round. IR£14 for groups of 16 upwards.
Hire facilities:	T Ca
Practice ground:	None
Catering:	Full catering 11.00am to 7.00pm. Later by arrangement.

*Dooks Golf Club:
view of the 1st*

view of the 7th

view of the 8th

KENMARE GOLF CLUB
(ESTABLISHED 1903)
Kenmare, Co. Kerry

Kenmare golf course is located in a magnificent sylvan setting where the cascading water of the Sheen and Roughty rivers join the Atlantic in Kenmare Bay. The course was developed over the years by dedicated local golfers together with the undoubted genius of Ireland's most experienced golf architect. Eddie Hackett has succeeded in creating an eighteen-hole golf course which can be very exacting for a great player but never unfair to the weak. A real test of golf in a unique golfing environment.

Secretary:	Manager: Micheál Fitzgerald; Sec: Siobhán O'Connor Tel 064 41291
Professional:	None
Type:	Parkland/links
No of holes:	18
Length:	5950 yards
Par:	71/70
Visitors:	Visitors welcome
Requirements:	🄷
Handicap Limits:	No beginners
Restrictions:	No restrictions, but enquire weekends. Weekdays are generally OK.
Parties:	Contact Micheál Fitzgerald
Green fees:	IR£12.50 per round. Groups of 18+ IR£10.
Hire facilities:	C T Ca
Practice ground:	Putting green. Driving range close by.
Catering:	Snacks only

Kenmare Golf Club

KILLARNEY GOLF AND FISHING CLUB

(ESTABLISHED 1893)

Mahony's Point, Killarney, Co. Kerry

The courses lie in an incomparable setting, winding around the shores of Lough Leane, and with the purple bulk of the Kerry mountains reflected in the clear water, it is difficult to imagine a more perfect place to play golf. In 1949 the Irish Amateur Open Championship was played at Killarney for the first time and there have been many major tournaments played there since that time. Gary Player rated the 13th on the Killeen course as "potentially one of the world's greatest inland golf holes". Another regular visitor to Killarney, Jimmy Bruen, is commemorated on the 2nd hole of Mahony.

Secretary:	Tom Prendergast Tel 064 31034/31242	
	Fax 064 33065	
Professional:	Tom Coveney Tel 064 31615	
	Course 1:	**Course 2:**
	Mahony's Point	Killeen
Type:	Parkland (lakeside)	Parkland (lakeside)
No of holes:	18	18
Length:	6867 yards	7126 yards
Par:	72	72
Visitors:	Visitors welcome	
Requirements:	H M	
Handicap Limits:	Gentlemen 28; Ladies 36; Juniors 36	
Restrictions:	None	
Parties:	Apply to Secretary	
Green fees:	IR£26 per round or per day (1994)	
Hire facilities:	C T Ca	
Practice ground:	Practice ground and putting area available	
Catering:	Dining facilities available	

Killarney Golf Club: views

KILLORGLIN GOLF COURSE
(ESTABLISHED 1992)
Stealrue, Killorglin, Co. Kerry

Killorglin is an eighteen-hole parkland course overlooking Dingle Bay and overshadowed by the majestic MacGillicuddy Reeks. Situated three kilometres from Killorglin town, just off the famous Ring of Kerry route on the N70 road.

Secretary:	Barry Harmon Tel 066 61979 Fax 066 61437
Professional:	None
Type:	Parkland
No of holes:	18
Length:	6464 yards
Par:	72
Visitors:	Visitors welcome
Requirements:	None
Handicap Limits:	None
Restrictions:	No restrictions. Booking necessary at weekends.
Parties:	Contact Mairead on 066 61979
Green fees:	IR£14 per round plus IR£5 for second round. Group rate IR£12 for ten persons or more.
Hire facilities:	C T Ca
Practice ground:	None
Catering:	Food available all day

Killorglin Golf Course

PARKNASILLA GOLF CLUB
(ESTABLISHED 1975)
Sneem, Co. Kerry

At present, renovations are taking place and the course will not be fully playable again until 1996.

Secretary:	Maurice Walsh Tel 064 45233
Professional:	Charlie McCarthy Tel 064 45172
Type:	Parkland
No of holes:	9 (played from outward and inward tees)
Length:	4894 yards
Par:	70
Visitors:	Visitors welcome
Requirements:	None
Handicap Limits:	None
Restrictions:	No restrictions for visitors
Parties:	Contact Parknasilla Great Southern Hotel on 064 45122
Green fees:	IR£9 per day. No special rates.
Hire facilities:	C B
Practice ground:	None
Catering:	Meals available at Great Southern Hotel, 10 minutes' walk from course.

TRALEE GOLF CLUB
(ESTABLISHED 1895)
West Barrow, Ardfert, Co. Kerry

The first Arnold Palmer designed course in Europe, the eighteen-hole layout spans 160 acres on the western side of 'Barrowe's Islande' from Poulgorm on the north to the Randy at Barrow Harbour on the south. The opening hole leads to a green overlooking the Long Strand featured in *Ryan's Daughter*. Below is the watery grave of the wreck *Onward of Swansea* (1877). The course has many scenic and picturesque holes with fine views of the Dingle Peninsula, Mount Brandon, Kerryhead, Ballyheigue, Banna and Carrahane. A great course, well worth a visit.

Secretary:	Peter Colleran Tel 066 36379 Fax 066 36008
Professional:	None
Type:	Links
No of holes:	18
Length:	6252 metres
Par:	71
Visitors:	Visitors welcome
Requirements:	H M
Handicap Limits:	Gentlemen 28; Ladies 36; Juniors 20
Restrictions:	Visitors: weekdays (except Wednesdays) 7.30am to 4.30pm. No visitors on Wednesdays in June, July, August 7.30 - 8.50am and 10.40 - 12.30pm or on Wednesdays in other months.
Parties:	Advance bookings required and deposit of IR£25 (non-refundable) to be received by club within two weeks of booking. 45 days' cancellation notice required. Credit cards acceptable.
Green fees:	IR£25 per round weekdays, IR£30 weekends. IR£15 second rounds. Students IR£15, G.U.I. IR£10.
Hire facilities:	T Ca Pc B
Practice ground:	Practice ground available
Catering:	Full bar and restaurant

Tralee Golf Club

WATERVILLE GOLF CLUB
(ESTABLISHED 1972)
Ring of Kerry, Waterville, Co. Kerry

One of the top five golf courses in Ireland and one of the top 50 in the world, having many memorable holes which have earned great praise from Gary Player, Ray Floyd and other professionals. The present course owes its start to John A. Mulcahy, an Irish American golf addict, who developed it with the aid of Eddie Hackett during the 1970s. Probably the best-known hole is the 17th, 'Mulcahy's Peak', a 196 yard par 3 with an elevated tee and an emerald green set in a jungle of rough. From the tee one can see the links set in the most perfect linksland in Europe. Not to be missed.

Secretary:	Mr Noel Cronin, Secretary/Manager Tel 066 74102/74545 Fax 066 74882
Professional:	Liam Higgins Tel 066 74102
Type:	Seaside links
No of holes:	18
Length:	7184 yards
Par:	72
Visitors:	Visitors welcome
Requirements:	H M
Handicap Limits:	Gentlemen 28; Ladies 36; Juniors 36
Restrictions:	No restrictions - tee times must be booked in advance
Parties:	Contact Reservations on 066 74102. All parties and societies welcome.
Green fees:	IR£35 per round (1994) Discount for groups of 20 or more. 1995 rates to be set in December 1994.
Hire facilities:	C T Ca B
Practice ground:	Driving range and putting green available
Catering:	Dining room/bar - full catering facilities. Accommodation available at Waterville House.

Waterville Golf Club: clubhouse

Waterville Golf course

ADARE MANOR GOLF CLUB
(ESTABLISHED 1900)
Adare, Co. Limerick

Historic castles are featured in a classic parkland setting.

Secretary:	Mr T. D. Healy, Hon. Sec. Tel 061 396204
Professional:	None
Type:	Parkland
No of holes:	18
Length:	5800 yards
Par:	69
Visitors:	Visitors welcome
Requirements:	None
Handicap Limits:	Gentlemen 28; Ladies 36; Juniors 36
Restrictions:	Gentlemen and Lady visitors on Saturday and Sunday by prior arrangement only
Parties:	Please contact Hon. Sec.
Green fees:	IR£15 per round. Special society rates available. Caddies by prior arrangement.
Hire facilities:	**C** **T** **Ca** (on request)
Practice ground:	No practice facilities
Catering:	Bar snacks

CASTLETROY GOLF CLUB
(ESTABLISHED 1937)
Castletroy, Co. Limerick

Parkland course featuring out of bounds on the left of the first two holes. Par 3 13th tee features panoramic view of the surrounding countryside. The par 4 18th is a stern finishing hole with the approach slightly uphill to a green guarded on both sides by bunkers. The club has hosted the Irish Finals of the Mixed Foursomes and 'Seniors' Championships in recent years in addition to numerous regional finals.

Secretary:	Laurence Hayes, Secretary/Manager
	Tel 061 335753 Fax 061 335373
Professional:	Noel Cassidy Tel 061 338283
Type:	Parkland
No of holes:	18
Length:	6335 yards (5793 metres)
Par:	71
Visitors:	Visitors welcome
Requirements:	None
Handicap Limits:	None
Restrictions:	All visitors restricted on Saturdays and Sundays except with member. Tuesday is Ladies Day - some restrictions. Ladies also restricted Thursday 11.00am to 3.00pm, and Juniors on Thursday afternoon.
Parties:	Contact Secretary/Manager for advance booking
Green fees:	IR£20 per day. Special rates on request.
Hire facilities:	**C** **T** **Ca** (on request) **B**
Practice ground:	None
Catering:	Full catering facilities

LIMERICK GOLF CLUB
(ESTABLISHED 1891)
Ballyclough, Co. Limerick

A well-groomed parkland course with a variety of trees. The club won the HAS Trophy European Clubs Cup Winners Championship in 1980, the only Irish club to win.

Secretary:	Declan McDonogh Tel 061 45146
Professional:	John Cassidy Tel 061 412492
Type:	Parkland
No of holes:	18
Length:	6532 yards (5938 metres)
Par:	72
Visitors:	Visitors welcome
Requirements:	H M
Handicap Limits:	Gentlemen 28; Ladies 36; Juniors 28
Restrictions:	Visitors welcome 8.30am to 4.00pm Monday, Wednesday, Thursday, Friday. No green fees accepted at weekends.
Parties:	Welcome on Monday, Wednesday and Friday:contact Secretary
Green fees:	IR£20 per day. IR£12 playing with a member.
Hire facilities:	C T Ca (by arrangement)
Practice ground:	Practice fairway and green
Catering:	Full catering facilities available 10.00am to 10.00pm

BALLYKISTEEN GOLF & COUNTRY CLUB
(ESTABLISHED 1994)
Ballykisteen, Monard, Co. Tipperary

Eighteen-hole championship course designed by Des Smyth and
Associates. Set in tree-scaped surroundings against the backdrop of the
beautiful Galtee mountains, lakes and streams help to make Ballykisteen
an idyllic setting of tranquillity. Bent and Fescue grasses together with
modern drainage methods ensure all-year-round golf. Forward tees are
provided leading to a course that is both playable and enjoyable for the
average golfer. This course is relatively new but has been received
exceptionally well by local golfers.

Secretary:	Contact Brian Begley Tel 062 51439
Professional:	None
Type:	Parkland
No of holes:	18
Length:	6765 yards
Par:	72
Visitors:	Visitors welcome
Requirements:	M preferred
Handicap Limits:	None
Restrictions:	No restrictions at present, unless there is an outing, or the course is busy
Parties:	Contact Brian Begley as above or 062 33222
Green fees:	IR£15 per rounds. Special rates depending on numbers.
Hire facilities:	T Ca (by appointment)
Practice ground:	Modern driving range and practice area
Catering:	Clubhouse facilities and dining will be available early in 1995

Ballykisteen Golf Club

CLONMEL GOLF CLUB
(ESTABLISHED 1911)
Lyreanearla, Mountain Road, Clonmel, Co. Tipperary

Set on the scenic slopes of the Comeragh Mountains just a short distance out of town, Clonmel golf course measures 5768 metres and is a testing course with features abounding. The clubhouse, built in 1984 with an alpine-like design, has appropriately a backdrop of fir and pine-covered mountains. "It's a highly enjoyable layout that remains largely unrecognised ... You get the feeling of getting away from it all with only the sound of streams babbling down from the mountains and the birds to interrupt the tranquility". (*Golf World*)

Secretary:	Aine Myles-Keating, Secretary/Manager Tel 052 24050
Professional:	Robert Hayes Tel 052 24050
Type:	Parkland
No of holes:	18
Length:	5768 metres
Par:	70
Visitors:	Visitors welcome
Requirements:	M
Handicap Limits:	None
Restrictions:	Monday is Ladies Day; Tuesday to Friday generally quiet. Saturday and Sunday by prior arrangement. Juniors not allowed Saturday and Sunday.
Parties:	Contact Secretary/Manager. Concessions for large groups.
Green fees:	IR£13 per round weekdays, IR£15 weekends. IR£10 with member.
Hire facilities:	**C** **T**
Practice ground:	Practice green and practice net
Catering:	Full catering and bar facilities

COUNTY TIPPERARY GOLF & COUNTRY CLUB
(ESTABLISHED 1993)
Dundrum House Hotel, Dundrum, Cashel, Co. Tipperary

The course is situated six miles west of Cashel in the heart of the Golden Vale, and incorporates the 18th-century manor Dundrum House Hotel, former seat of the Earls of Montalt. It occupies 170 acres and was designed by tour professional Philip Walton, who has used the natural features of woodland, parkland and the gently-flowing Multeen River to create a testing par 72 course in the most beautiful setting.

Secretary:	Seamus King Tel 062 61307
Professional:	William Crowe, Course Manager Tel 062 71116/71366
Type:	Parkland
No of holes:	18
Length:	6709 yards (6150 metres)
Par:	72
Visitors:	Visitors welcome
Requirements:	None
Handicap Limits:	None
Restrictions:	No restrictions, but ring Course Manager in advance for weekend bookings
Parties:	Please contact William Crowe, Course Manager
Green fees:	Midweek IR£15 per round, weekends IR£20. Special rates for parties available on request.
Hire facilities:	**C** **T** **Ca** (on request)
Practice ground:	Practice green. Driving range ¼ mile away.
Catering:	The course is in the grounds of Dundrum House Hotel, which is a Grade A Hotel with a highly acclaimed restaurant to suit all tastes.

Co. Tipperary Golf Club: the 9th hole

NENAGH GOLF CLUB
(ESTABLISHED 1929)
Beechwood, Nenagh, Co. Tipperary

Nenagh golf course is situated five miles north-east of the town of Nenagh and is laid out on free-draining ground, making it playable all the year round. The Club has just purchased a further parcel of land with the long-term intention of having 27 holes.

Secretary:	Murdo Morrison Tel 067 31476
Professional:	John Coyle Tel 067 33242
Type:	Parkland
No of holes:	18
Length:	6006 yards (5491 metres)
Par:	69
Visitors:	Visitors welcome
Requirements:	H M
Handicap Limits:	Gentlemen 28; Ladies 36; Juniors 28
Restrictions:	All visitors restricted on Saturdays and Sundays depending on club competitions.
Parties:	Contact Michael Corcoran
Green fees:	IR£12 per day weekdays. IR£15 weekends.
Hire facilities:	C T
Practice ground:	Extensive 20-acre practice ground
Catering:	Full catering and restaurant facilities

ROSCREA GOLF CLUB
(ESTABLISHED 1892)
Derryvale, Roscrea, Co. Tipperary

Roscrea Golf Club is situated on the main Dublin/Limerick Road, the N7. It is an ideal place to break your journey to play a game of golf and have lunch or snack. A special feature of the course is the variety of the par 3 holes, most noteworthy of which is the 180-yard 6th, which is played almost entirely over a lake. The most famous hole on the course is the new 7th, referred to locally as 'The Burma Road' - a par 5 of over 500 yards with magnificent trees on both sides and out of bounds all along the left hand side.

Secretary:	Kieran McDonnell Tel 0505 21518
Professional:	None
Type:	Parkland
No of holes:	18
Length:	5750 metres
Par:	71
Visitors:	Visitors always welcome
Requirements:	None
Handicap Limits:	None
Restrictions:	No restrictions
Parties:	Please contact the Secretary
Green fees:	IR£10 per day weekdays, IR£12 Saturday and Sunday
Hire facilities:	T
Practice ground:	None
Catering:	Full catering facilities

THURLES GOLF CLUB
(ESTABLISHED 1909)
Turtulla, Thurles, Co. Tipperary

Thurles is a parkland course with terrain generally level, excellent greens and wide fairways. The rough is lush and holding. The course is well-sheltered and divided by a main road with nine holes on either side. It is located on the N62 just over half a mile (about 1km) south of Thurles on the Horse and Jockey Road. Thurles is situated in the heartland of County Tipperary, close to the Rock of Cashel and Holycross Abbey. The club also has two championship squash courts.

Secretary:	Thomas Ryan Tel 0504 23787
Professional:	Sean Hunt Tel 0504 21983
Type:	Parkland
No of holes:	18
Length:	6445 yards (5904 metres)
Par:	72
Visitors:	Visitors welcome
Requirements:	None
Handicap Limits:	None
Restrictions:	Limited availability at weekends. Tuesday is Ladies Day. Juniors must be off the course at 6.00pm.
Parties:	Contact Thomas Ryan
Green fees:	IR£15 per round. No special rates.
Hire facilities:	C T Ca B
Practice ground:	Driving range 200 yards from club
Catering:	Full catering facilities available. Contact Steward, Conor Hewitt.

DUNMORE EAST GOLF CLUB
(ESTABLISHED 1993)
Dunmore East, Co. Waterford

The course overlooks the village of Dunmore East with panoramic views of the village and bay, the Hook peninsula and Waterford Harbour Estuary. The first nine holes were opened in June 1993 and a further nine holes are due for completion in 1994 to make an eighteen-hole, 6236 yard, par 72 course, which promises to offer idyllic surroundings, sea air and stimulating, challenging golf for both the high and low handicapper. Dunmore East is renowned for its excellent accommodation and superb food.

Secretary:	Mary Skehan Tel 051 383151
Professional:	None
Type:	Seaside parkland
No of holes:	9
Length:	2408 yards (2201 metres)
Par:	33
Visitors:	Visitors welcome
Requirements:	None
Handicap Limits:	None
Restrictions:	No restrictions for visitors
Parties:	Please contact Mary Skehan, Secretary
Green fees:	IR£6 - IR£10 per round, IR£10 per day. For groups of six or more IR£6 for 9 holes, IR£8 for eighteen holes.
Hire facilities:	C T Ca
Practice ground:	None
Catering:	Snacks available all day. Lunch/dinner arranged with local hostelries all within half a mile of the golf course.

Dunmore East Golf and Country Club: views

FAITHLEGG GOLF CLUB
(ESTABLISHED 1993)
Faithlegg House, Co. Waterford

Course opened for play on May 1st 1993 and is located six miles from
Waterford City. Set amidst the tree-scaped surrounds of Faithlegg, the
course is just under 7000 yards from the championship tees. Some wicked
slopes and borrows on the immaculate greens, plus undulating fairways
and strategically placed water hazards are just some of the features packed
into this Paddy Merrigan designed course; he sensitively integrated the
course into a landscape textured with mature trees and flowing parkland.
The classic site on the banks of the River Suir is ideal for players seeking a
golf challenge.

Secretary:	Miss Vari McGreevy Tel 051 82441/82688
	Fax 051 82664
Professional:	Ted Higgins Tel as for Sec.
Type:	Parkland
No of holes:	18
Length:	6057 metres
Par:	72
Visitors:	Visitors always welcome
Requirements:	H
Handicap Limits:	None
Restrictions:	No restrictions for visitors
Parties:	Contact Vari McGreevy: special rates for groups of 20+
Green fees:	IR£20 per round (IR£16 before 9.00am). IR£27 per day. Juniors and Students IR£12. Golf and dinner IR£27.
Hire facilities:	C T Ca B
Practice ground:	Practice ground and putting green
Catering:	Full bar and restaurant facilities every day

Faithlegg Golf Club

LISMORE GOLF CLUB
(ESTABLISHED 1965)
Ballyin, Lismore, Co. Waterford

Nine-hole course on the banks of the Blackwater River beneath the shade of Lismore Castle, seat of the Duke of Devonshire. Visitors welcome at all times except Sunday mornings and Wednesday (Ladies Day) to this delightful well-maintained course.

Secretary:	Shaun Moynihan Tel 058 54016
Professional:	None
Type:	Manicured parkland
No of holes:	9 (played from outward and inward tees)
Length:	5291 metres
Par:	69
Visitors:	Visitors welcome
Requirements:	None
Handicap Limits:	Gentlemen 28; Ladies 36; Juniors 36
Restrictions:	Gentlemen restricted on Wednesdays - Ladies Day. Ladies and Juniors restricted on Sunday mornings.
Parties:	Contact Hon. Sec. for society arrangements and reductions
Green fees:	IR£8 weekdays, IR£10 weekends. Special rates for societies.
Hire facilities:	T
Practice ground:	Driving area (250 metres). Practice green.
Catering:	Bar open 10.00am to 5.00pm in summer

TRAMORE GOLF CLUB
(ESTABLISHED 1894)
Newtown Hill, Tramore, Co. Waterford

The present course was designed by Captain H. C. Tippett of Wimbledon Golf Club and was opened in June 1939 - the previous location being an unsatisfactory links area near the sea and the race course. The view from the clubhouse is magnificent, embracing as it does the whole course with the lofty Comeragh Mountains in the distant background. The site is gently undulating, and intercepted by two streams. A first-class golf course, excellent clubhouse facilities and a friendly welcome for any visitor wishing a tough test of golf in an ideal environment.

Secretary:	James Cox, Secretary/Manager Tel 051 86170
Professional:	Paul McDaid Tel 051 81706
Type:	Parkland
No of holes:	18
Length:	6622 yards (6055 metres)
Par:	72
Visitors:	Visitors welcome
Requirements:	H M
Handicap Limits:	Gentlemen 28; Ladies 36
Restrictions:	Visitors tee times strictly by arrangement with Secretary/Manager's office (051 86170). Avoid Sundays.
Parties:	Contact James Cox - prior booking required
Green fees:	IR£17 per round midweek, IR£20 weekends
Hire facilities:	C T Ca
Practice ground:	Two practice areas, one adjacent to clubhouse
Catering:	Full catering facilities are available

Tramore Golf Club: clubhouse

WATERFORD GOLF CLUB
(ESTABLISHED 1912)
Newrath, Waterford, Co. Waterford

Attractive parkland course designed by the great James Braid. Waterford is particularly renowned for the quality of its greens and for its friendly atmosphere. The first nine demands accuracy from the tee. The back nine is more forgiving and features a great closing stretch with a classic finishing hole. Here the drive is struck from an elevated tee with an all-round view to a narrow fairway which winds its way downhill, between score-threatening gorse, to a receptive green 400 yards away.

Secretary:	John Colfer Tel 051 76748 Fax 051 53405
Professional:	Eamonn Condon Tel 051 54256
Type:	Parkland
No of holes:	18
Length:	6237 yards (5722 metres)
Par:	71
Visitors:	Visitors welcome
Requirements:	M
Handicap Limits:	None
Restrictions:	Gentlemen and juniors restricted on Tuesdays. Ladies restricted on Wednesdays.
Parties:	Please contact J. Condon, Sec/Manager
Green fees:	IR£15 per round. No special or daily rates.
Hire facilities:	C T Ca Pc B
Practice ground:	Large practice ground and putting green
Catering:	Full catering facilities available

WATERFORD CASTLE GOLF CLUB
(ESTABLISHED 1992)
The Island, Waterford, Co. Waterford

Designed by Des Smyth and Associates, the course offers a unique experience to any discerning golfer. Ireland's only true island course and yet within two miles of Waterford city centre, it was laid out on 250 acres of lush parkland and incorporates four artificial lakes which fit well into the wooded landscape. The course is a fine test of golf, requiring accuracy and length; the superb sand-based and well-bunkered greens provide an excellent all-year round challenge. A visit to Waterford Castle is recommended for golf in really pleasant surroundings.

Secretary:	Dick Brennan Tel 051 71633
Professional:	None
Type:	Parkland
No of holes:	18
Length:	6209 metres
Par:	72
Visitors:	Visitors welcome
Requirements:	None
Handicap Limits:	None
Restrictions:	Members reserved tee times are 8.30 - 10.00am and 2.00 - 2.30pm, otherwise no restriction for visitors but subject to pre-booking and availability.
Parties:	Please contact Ann Dempsey (Office Manager) or Secretary
Green fees:	IR£20 per round. No day rates. Group discounts by negotiation.
Hire facilities:	C T Ca
Practice ground:	Putting green available
Catering:	Dining facilities available

WEST WATERFORD GOLF CLUB
(ESTABLISHED 1993)

Coolcormak, Dungarvan, Co. Waterford

The West Waterford Golf Club is built on 150 acres of rolling parkland on
the banks of the Brickey river with the backdrop of the Comeragh
Mountains to the east, the Knockmealdowns to the north and Drum Hills
to the south. An interesting feature is that the first nine holes are laid out
on a large plateau featuring a lovely stream which comes into play at the
3rd and 4th holes. The Brickey river traverses the southern boundary and
features the 2nd, 12th, 14th, 15th, and 16th holes which makes these very
challenging. Designed by Eddie Hackett.

Secretary:	Nora J. Spratt Tel 058 43216 Fax 058 44343
Professional:	To be appointed
Type:	Parkland
No of holes:	18
Length:	6771 yards (6162 metres)
Par:	72
Visitors:	Visitors welcome
Requirements:	[H] (if possible)
Handicap Limits:	None
Restrictions:	No restrictions - pre-booking appreciated
Parties:	Contact Secretary
Green fees:	IR£15 weekdays, IR£20 weekends, per round. Discounts arranged for groups/societies.
Hire facilities:	[C] [T] [Ca] [B]
Practice ground:	Four-acre practice ground on course
Catering:	Full restaurant and bar facilities all day every day

ULSTER: NORTHERN IRELAND GOLF CLUBS

Co. Antrim
Ballycastle
Ballyclare
Ballymena
Cairndhu
Carrickfergus
Cushendall
Lisburn
Massereene
Royal Portrush
Whitehead

Co. Armagh
County Armagh
Lurgan
Portadown
Silverwood
Tandragee

Co. Down
Ardglass
Balmoral
Banbridge
Bangor
Belvoir Park
Bright Castle
Carnalea
Clandeboye
Cliftonville
Donaghadee
Downpatrick
Dunmurry
Holywood
Kirkistown Castle
Knock
Malone
Mount Ober
Royal Belfast
Royal County Down
Scrabo
Shandon Park
Spa
Warrenpoint

Co. Fermanagh
Enniskillen

Co. Londonderry
Castlerock
City of Derry
Moyola Park
Portstewart

Co. Tyrone
Dungannon
Killymoon
Omagh
Strabane

BALLYCASTLE GOLF CLUB
(ESTABLISHED 1890)
Cushendall Road, Ballycastle, Co. Antrim, BT64 6QP

The first five holes are parkland along the banks of the Margy and Carey rivers and bordering the ruins of a 13th-century friary. The Warren area is six holes of true links, and the inward seven are in adjacent upland with panoramic views including the Mull of Kintyre, Rathlin Island and Ballycastle Bay. The course demands accurate irons.

Secretary:	Mr N. E. Page Tel 02657 62536
Professional:	Mr I. McLaughlin Tel 02657 62506
Type:	Parkland/links
No of holes:	18
Length:	5882 yards (5376 metres)
Par:	71
Visitors:	Visitors welcome
Requirements:	None
Handicap Limits:	None
Restrictions:	Restricted at weekends
Parties:	Contact Hon. Secretary - no special provisions
Green fees:	£13 per round weekday. £28 per round weekends and public holidays.
Hire facilities:	T
Practice ground:	None
Catering:	Facilites available in clubhouse

Ballycastle Golf Club

BALLYCLARE GOLF CLUB
(ESTABLISHED 1923)
25 Springvale Road, Ballyclare, Co. Antrim

Parkland course with most fairways tree-lined. Natural river or burn meandering through the course. Two lakes between 3rd and 7th fairways.

Secretary:	Harry McConnell Tel 0960 322696
Professional:	Stephen Hamill Tel 0960 322416
Type:	Parkland
No of holes:	18
Length:	6282 yards (5745 metres)
Par:	71
Visitors:	Visitors welcome
Requirements:	None
Handicap Limits:	Gentlemen 20; Ladies 36; Juniors 20
Restrictions:	Gentlemen - restricted Thursdays; Ladies - restricted Saturday and Sunday morning; Juniors - restricted after 4.30pm weekdays.
Parties:	Contact Secretary
Green fees:	£14 per round weekdays, £20 Saturdays and Sundays. Parties over 20 £12.
Hire facilities:	T
Practice ground:	Practice fairway, green, bunker and putting green
Catering:	Dining facilities available

BALLYMENA GOLF CLUB
(ESTABLISHED 1903)
128 Raceview Road, Broughshane, Ballymena, Co. Antrim, BT42 4HY

Just a mile from the picturesque village of Broughshane, winners of
'Europe in Bloom', and 2$\frac{1}{2}$ miles east of Ballymena on A42 is the
Ballymena Golf Club. It is a flat heathland course, with heathers and gorse
and lined with trees. On the eastern side is the famous St. Patrick's
Slemish mountain.

Secretary:	Carl McAuley Tel 0266 861487
Professional:	Ken Revie, Teaching Pro.
Type:	Heathland
No of holes:	18
Length:	5245 metres
Par:	68
Visitors:	Visitors welcome
Requirements:	None
Handicap Limits:	Gentlemen 26; Ladies 36
Restrictions:	Visitors restricted all day Saturday. Ladies Day - Tuesday. Juniors not allowed after 6.00pm except Sundays.
Parties:	Please contact Secretary
Green fees:	£13 per day weekdays (£8 with member). £16 per day Sunday and holidays (£9 with member).
Hire facilities:	**T**
Practice ground:	None
Catering:	Excellent catering facilities and bar snacks

CAIRNDHU GOLF CLUB
(ESTABLISHED 1928)
192 Coast Road, Ballygally, Larne, Co. Antrim, BT40 2QC

A parkland course with spectacular views.

Secretary:	Mrs J. Robinson Tel 0574 583324
Professional:	Mr R. Walker Tel 0574 583417
Type:	Parkland
No of holes:	18
Length:	6112 yards (5598 metres)
Par:	70
Visitors:	Visitors welcome
Requirements:	None
Handicap Limits:	None
Restrictions:	No visitors on Saturdays. Weekdays: visitors to be off first tee by 4.30pm.
Parties:	Contact Mrs J. Robinson
Green fees:	£12 per round or per day. Sundays £20 per day.
Hire facilities:	**C** **T**
Practice ground:	None
Catering:	Bar snacks and dining room meals available

Cairndhu Golf Club

CARRICKFERGUS GOLF CLUB
(ESTABLISHED 1926)
35, North Road, Carrickfergus, Co. Antrim, BT38 8LP

Located half a mile from Carrickfergus via Albert Road. The first hole requires a difficult shot over a large dam, but this degree of difficulty is not maintained in the remaining holes of this very pleasant parkland course.

Secretary:	Mr R. J. Campbell, Secretary/Manager Tel 0960 363713
Professional:	Raymond Stevenson Tel 0960 351803
Type:	Parkland
No of holes:	18
Length:	5765 yards
Par:	68
Visitors:	Visitors welcome
Requirements:	None
Handicap Limits:	Gentlemen 24; Ladies 36; Juniors 36
Restrictions:	Visitors restricted after 1.00pm Fridays and on Saturdays and Sundays. Ladies not allowed on Saturdays during Gentlemen's competitions.
Parties:	Please contact Secretary/Manager
Green fees:	£18 per round
Hire facilities:	C T
Practice ground:	None
Catering:	Full dining facilities available

CUSHENDALL GOLF CLUB
(ESTABLISHED 1937)
Shore Road, Cushendall, Co. Antrim

25 miles north of Larne on Antrim coast road. Follow signs for Beach/Golf Course from middle of Cushendall Village. Tree-lined course through which the picturesque River Dall meanders and comes into play on seven of the nine holes - making out of bounds a distinct possibility. This relatively short course requires accurate shots. Superb views of Scotland's Mull of Kintyre across the Sea of Moyle, and Antrim heathlands looking inland. The Club motif relates to ancient Irish Legend, 'The Children of Lir', who were turned into swans and set adrift on the Sea of Moyle for 300 years.

Secretary:	Shaun McLaughlin Tel 0266 758366
Professional:	None
Type:	Parkland
No of holes:	9
Length:	2193 metres
Par:	33
Visitors:	Visitors welcome
Requirements:	None
Handicap Limits:	None
Restrictions:	Ladies Day is Thursday (preference given). Time sheets operate on Saturday and Sunday. Visitors welcome at all times by arrangement.
Parties:	Please contact V. Agnew c/o Cushendall Golf Club
Green fees:	£10 per day (£3 with member).
Hire facilities:	None
Practice ground:	Small practice area, sand bunker and putting green
Catering:	Full catering service high season. By arrangement during low season.

LISBURN GOLF CLUB
(ESTABLISHED 1891)
68, Eglantine Road, Lisburn, Co Antrim, BT27 5RQ

Eighteen-hole parkland course with fine views over Lagan Valley.

Secretary:	George Graham Tel 0846 677216
	Fax 0846 603608
Professional:	Blake Campbell Tel 0846 677217
Type:	Parkland
No of holes:	18
Length:	6647 yards
Par:	72
Visitors:	Visitors welcome
Requirements:	None
Handicap Limits:	None
Restrictions:	All visitors restricted before 3.00pm on weekdays and after 5.00pm on Saturdays. No visitors on Sunday except with member.
Parties:	Please contact Secretary
Green fees:	£25 per round. Special rates for parties over 20.
Hire facilities:	C T Pc
Practice ground:	Practice ground available
Catering:	Full range of meals all day

Lisburn Golf Club

MASSEREENE GOLF CLUB
(ESTABLISHED 1895)
51, Lough Road, Antrim, BT41 4DQ

The club is close to Belfast International Airport with the course running along the shores of Lough Neagh, the biggest inland stretch of water in the British Isles. The existing course was laid out by Fred Hawtree in 1961, and the opening holes wind away from the clubhouse until the par 5 7th which goes downhill to the shoreline of the lake in the direction of Shane's Castle. There are other good holes on the front nine before crossing the road to the second nine on the more sandy ground mainly along the shoreline. Slice your ball on the 10th and you'll be out of bounds in the Antrim Stadium!

Secretary:	Mrs Marie Agnew, Secretary/Manager
	Tel 0849 428096
Professional:	Jim Smyth Tel 0849 464074
Type:	Parkland
No of holes:	18
Length:	6559 yards
Par:	72
Visitors:	Visitors welcome
Requirements:	None
Handicap Limits:	Gentlemen 28; Ladies 36; Juniors 36
Restrictions:	Ladies and Gentlemen restricted Fridays and Saturdays only. Juniors restricted in summer after 4.45pm weekdays and before 4.00pm weekends and public holidays.
Parties:	Contact Secretary/Manager
Green fees:	£18 per day weekdays, £23 weekends. No special rates.
Hire facilities:	C T
Practice ground:	Practice putting green only
Catering:	Snacks and dining room meals available

ROYAL PORTRUSH GOLF CLUB
(ESTABLISHED 1888)

Dunluce Road, Portrush, Co. Antrim, BT56 8JQ

Royal Portrush is situated one hour's drive from Belfast airport and from the ferry port at Larne. It is surrounded by the Giant's Causeway, beautiful white sandy beaches and rolling green countryside. The course was redesigned by H. S. Colt in 1947 and saw the first Open Championship ever held in Ireland in July 1951. The Dunluce course has been portrayed by many golfers as one of the most challenging courses in the world. It is testing, requiring skill and concentration, but set in one of the most scenic parts of Europe, the most notable holes being the 5th, 10th, 3rd and 17th.

Secretary:	Miss W. I. Erskine Tel 0265 823139	
	Fax 0265 822311	
Professional:	Dai Stevenson Tel 0265 822285	
	Course 1: Dunluce	**Course 2:** Valley
Type:	Parkland	Parkland
No of holes:	18	18
Length:	6650 yards	6054 yards
Par:	73	70

Visitors:	Visitors welcome
Requirements:	H
Handicap Limits:	Gentlemen 24; Ladies 36
Restrictions:	Sunday no visitors prior to 10.00am. Saturday no visitors until 2.00pm. Monday to Friday reserved for members 12.30 to 2.00pm. Ladies as above except Saturday and Sunday. Juniors must be accompanied by an adult.
Parties:	Contact Secretary/Manager for booking. No special rates.
Green fees:	Dunluce Monday to Friday £37.50 per day; Saturday, Sunday and Band Holidays £45. Valley Monday to Friday £15 per day; Saturday, Sunday and public holidays £20.
Hire facilities:	C T Ca

Practice ground:	Two practice grounds. Also nine-hole course.
Catering:	Snack menu available all day. Function menu available if required. Sunday carvery lunch.

Royal Portrush Golf Club

Score card details: Dunluce

Hole	1	2	3	4	5	6	7	8	9	10	11	12	13	14	15	16	17	18
Yds	381	493	150	454	386	191	420	365	476	477	166	389	366	205	361	415	508	477
Par	4	5	3	4	4	3	4	4	5	5	3	4	4	3	4	4	5	5

Score card details: Valley

Hole	1	2	3	4	5	6	7	8	9	10	11	12	13	14	15	16	17	18
Yds	339	374	135	520	324	231	441	399	311	472	130	452	458	412	155	349	382	170
Par	4	4	3	5	4	4	4	4	4	5	3	4	5	4	3	4	4	3

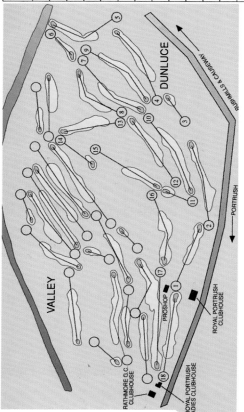

Royal Portrush Golf Club: course plan

WHITEHEAD GOLF CLUB
(ESTABLISHED 1904)
McCrae's Brae, Whitehead, Carrickfergus, Co. Antrim, BT38 9NZ

A good seaside/parkland eighteen-hole course with fine views of the sea.

Secretary:	Mr J. M. Niblock, Secretary/Manager
	Tel 0960 353631
Professional:	Mr T. Loughran Tel 0960 353118
Type:	Parkland
No of holes:	18
Length:	6362 yards
Par:	72
Visitors:	Visitors welcome
Requirements:	None
Handicap Limits:	None
Restrictions:	No visitors on Saturdays. Visitors on Sunday with member only. Monday to Friday tee reserved for members 12.30 - 1.30 and no visitors after 4.30 except with member. Juniors must be accompanied by an adult.
Parties:	Please contact Secretary/Manager
Green fees:	£11 per round
Hire facilities:	None
Practice ground:	None
Catering:	Bar Snacks available. *A la carte* meals can be arranged with the Steward.

COUNTY ARMAGH GOLF CLUB
(ESTABLISHED 1893)
Newry Road, Armagh, Armagh

Fairly short eighteen-hole parkland course with plenty of trees and a stream.

Secretary:	Philip Reid Tel 0861 525861
Professional:	Alan Rankin Tel 0861 525864
Type:	Parkland
No of holes:	18
Length:	5649 metres
Par:	70
Visitors:	Visitors welcome
Requirements:	None
Handicap Limits:	None
Restrictions:	Gentlemen, Ladies and Juniors not admitted during competitions, society outings and weekends
Parties:	Contact Brian Hughes, Society Convenor at club
Green fees:	£12 per round weekdays. £18 weekends and public holidays.
Hire facilities:	C T Pc
Practice ground:	Driving range
Catering:	Tuesday to Sunday

LURGAN GOLF CLUB
(ESTABLISHED 1893)
The Demesne, Lurgan, Co. Armagh, BT67 9BN

Straightness and accuracy off the tee is an essential for this testing eighteen-hole parkland course.

Secretary:	Gail Turkington Tel 0762 322087
Professional:	Des Paul Tel 0762 321068
Type:	Parkland
No of holes:	18
Length:	5836 metres
Par:	70
Visitors:	Visitors welcome
Requirements:	H (open competitions only)
Handicap Limits:	None
Restrictions:	Gentlemen: Mondays, Thursdays and Fridays best. Not Saturday except after 5.00pm. Ladies: avoid Wednesdays and Saturdays.
Parties:	Contact Secretary's office for details
Green fees:	Monday - Friday £15 per round. Saturday, Sunday and public holidays £20 per round. Special rates for societies.
Hire facilities:	None
Practice ground:	Practice ground and putting green available
Catering:	Full catering facility

Score card details

Hole	1	2	3	4	5	6	7	8	9	10	11	12	13	14	15	16	17	18
Yds	258	214	113	371	387	504	390	152	528	298	158	355	448	376	394	410	125	355
Par	4	3	3	4	4	5	4	3	5	4	3	4	5	4	4	4	3	4

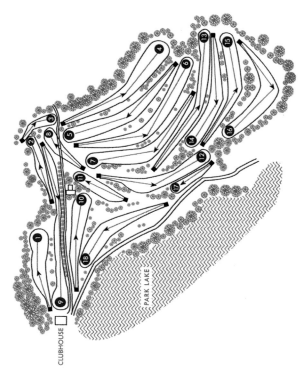

Lurgan Golf Club: course plan

PORTADOWN GOLF CLUB
(ESTABLISHED 1900)

192 Gilford Road, Portadown, Co. Armagh, BT63 5LF

Portadown is a very attractively laid-out eighteen-hole parkland course.

Secretary:	Mrs M. E. Holloway　Tel 0762 355356
Professional:	Mr P. Stevenson　Tel 0762 334655
Type:	Parkland
No of holes:	18
Length:	5649 metres
Par:	70
Visitors:	Visitors welcome
Requirements:	None
Handicap Limits:	None
Restrictions:	Visitors are welcome on Mondays up to 3.00pm, Wednesdays and Thursdays no later than 12 noon, Fridays up to 3.00pm and Saturdays after 4.30pm.
Parties:	Please contact Mrs. M. E. Holloway
Green fees:	£15 per round weekday, £18 weekends and public holidays. Societies £12 weekdays and £16 Sundays and public holidays.
Hire facilities:	🛒
Practice ground:	Practice area and putting green
Catering:	Restaurant and bar snacks

SILVERWOOD GOLF CLUB
(ESTABLISHED 1974)
Lurgan, Co. Armagh

This is a parkland course owned and run by the borough council, to whom all queries regarding play should be addressed as follows: Recreation Department Craigavon Borough Council, Larkview Road, Craigavon.

Secretary:	Colin McKerr
Professional:	None
Type:	Parkland
No of holes:	18
Length:	6459 yards
Par:	72
Visitors:	Visitors welcome
Requirements:	[M]
Handicap Limits:	Gentlemen 28
Restrictions:	All visitors restricted 8.30 - 11.00am; Saturdays and Sundays.
Parties:	Contact to be made with Craigavon Borough Council
Green fees:	By arrangement with Borough Council
Hire facilities:	[C]
Practice ground:	None
Catering:	Catering facilities available

TANDRAGEE GOLF CLUB
(ESTABLISHED 1920)
Market Hill Road, Tandragee, Craigavon, Co. Armagh, BT62 2ER

The course was developed on the Duke of Manchester's estate in 1911 and the club formed in 1920. The present clubhouse was built in 1980 and extended in 1990. The course is hilly with magnificent views of the Mourne mountains and South Armagh, and because the soil is of a sandy texture is playable in the wettest weather. Conveniently located approximately eight miles from Portadown on A27 to Newry and ten miles from the cathedral city of Armagh.

Secretary:	Hal McCready Tel 0762 841272
Professional:	Erill Maney Tel 0762 841761
Type:	Parkland
No of holes:	18
Length:	5446 metres
Par:	69
Visitors:	Visitors welcome
Requirements:	None
Handicap Limits:	None
Restrictions:	Gentlemen: Saturday all day. Ladies: Thursdays not after 2.00pm. Juniors: as for Gentlemen and Ladies.
Parties:	Please contact Secretary/Manager. No societies on Mondays and Saturdays, and restricted to 10.30 - 11.30am Sundays.
Green fees:	£12 per day weekdays, £18 Sundays and public holidays. Societies £11.
Hire facilities:	[C] [T]
Practice ground:	Putting green and pitching area
Catering:	Full catering and bar facilities

ARDGLASS GOLF CLUB
(ESTABLISHED 1896)
Castle Place, Ardglass, Co. Down, BT30 7TP

One of the most spectacular scenic courses in Ireland with several tees and
greens overlooking the Irish Sea to the Isle of Man. The Mountains of
Mourne are only 12 miles away and the clubhouse is a converted historic
15th-century castle with the sea lapping the walls. There are many
memorable holes - in particular the par 3 2nd of 161 yards, which requires
a tee shot across a deep inlet with the sea pounding beneath.

Secretary:	Alan Cannon Tel 0396 841219
	Fax 0396 841841
Professional:	Kevan Whitson Tel 0396 841022
Type:	Seaside
No of holes:	18
Length:	6048 yards
Par:	70
Visitors:	Visitors welcome
Requirements:	None
Handicap Limits:	None
Restrictions:	All visitors restricted at weekends
Parties:	Please contact the Secretary
Green fees:	Weekdays £15 per day. Weekends £20 per round.
	Societies £14 per round weekday, £20 weekends.
Hire facilities:	[C] [T]
Practice ground:	None available
Catering:	Bar snacks available daily. *A la carte* evenings.

BALMORAL GOLF CLUB LTD
(ESTABLISHED 1914)
The Club House, Balmoral, Belfast, BT9 6GX

Location two miles south of Belfast city centre. Flat course, par 69. The clubhouse was built in 1988 and has received a design award.

Secretary:	Robert C. McConkey, Manager
	Tel 0232 381514
Professional:	Mr G. Bleakley Tel 0232 669505
Type:	Parkland
No of holes:	18
Length:	5488 metres
Par:	69
Visitors:	Visitors welcome
Requirements:	None
Handicap Limits:	None
Restrictions:	Visitors cannot play before 2.00pm on Sundays or on Saturdays before 3.30pm in winter and 4.30pm in summer
Parties:	Contact Robert C. McConkey, General Manager
Green fees:	£20 per round. Societies over 20: 10% reduction.
Hire facilities:	C T
Practice ground:	Small practice area
Catering:	Catering and bar facilities

BANBRIDGE GOLF CLUB
(ESTABLISHED 1913)
Huntly Road, Banbridge, Co. Down, BT32 3UR

The course has recently been extended to eighteen holes, including the dogleg 'Pond' hole – the 6th. The redesigned par 5 14th requires a tricky shot over a ravine. The par 3 10th is also tough: 201 metres, with the green very close to the boundary hedge. The course is located one mile from the town centre on Huntly Road.

Secretary:	Mr T. A. Wilson (Hon. Sec.); Mrs. J. A. Antekell, Administrator Tel 08206 62211
Professional:	None
Type:	Parkland
No of holes:	18
Length:	5000 metres
Par:	69
Visitors:	Visitors welcome
Requirements:	None
Handicap Limits:	Gentlemen 26; Ladies 36; Juniors 36
Restrictions:	Gentlemen restricted only during competitions (Saturdays) and Ladies Day (Tuesday). Ladies restricted during men's competitions and on Saturdays.
Parties:	Contact Mrs J. A. Anketell
Green fees:	Gentlemen £15 per round weekdays, £20 Saturday, Sunday and public holidays. Ladies £12 per round (£15 per day) and Juniors £4 per round.
Hire facilities:	None
Practice ground:	None
Catering:	Catering facilities available

BANGOR GOLF CLUB
(ESTABLISHED 1903)
Broadway, Bangor, Co. Down, BT20 4RH, Co. Down

Bangor Golf Club is located about one mile from Bangor town centre and the railway and bus stations. An extensive tree-planting programme means the course places great emphasis on accuracy. There are fine views over Belfast Lough to Scotland from the centre of the course. Bangor was the venue for the 1993 Irish Amateur Seniors Championship.

Secretary:	Mr T. Russell Tel 0247 270922
Professional:	Norman V. Drew Tel 0247 462164
Type:	Parkland
No of holes:	18
Length:	6424 yards
Par:	71
Visitors:	Visitors welcome
Requirements:	H M
Handicap Limits:	None
Restrictions:	All visitors: no Saturday play and no play between 1.00 and 2.00pm Monday to Friday, or on Tuesdays (Ladies Day). Ladies and Juniors not before 6.00pm Monday to Friday.
Parties:	Mondays and Wednesdays only. Not Saturday or Sunday nor between 1.00 - 2.00pm Monday to Friday unless by special arrangement. Contact the General Manager.
Green fees:	£17 per day. Societies of 20 or more: £15 Monday to Thursday, £17 Friday.
Hire facilities:	C T
Practice ground:	Practice ground including green. Two putting greens.
Catering:	Full catering Monday - Friday, April - September. Tuesday - Friday October - March.

Score card details

Hole	1	2	3	4	5	6	7	8	9	10	11	12	13	14	15	16	17	18
Yds	343	482	349	461	465	353	181	401	384	416	309	176	374	163	405	481	150	326
Par	4	5	4	5	4	4	3	4	4	4	4	3	4	3	4	5	3	4

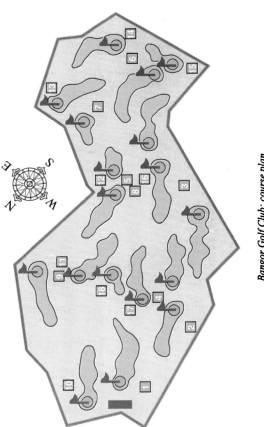

Bangor Golf Club: course plan

BELVOIR PARK GOLF CLUB
(ESTABLISHED 1927)
73, Church Road, Newtownbreda, Belfast, BT8 4AN

Championship standard inland golf course. Most holes lined with mature trees on an undulating terrain, but not physically demanding. The course is rather unusual in modern days in that it has five short holes. This is well balanced by quite a few long par 4s. The holes from the 15th to 18th give one of the most demanding finishes on an inland course in Ireland.

Secretary:	Kenneth H. Graham Tel 0232 491693
Professional:	Maurice Kelly Tel 0232 646714
Type:	Parkland
No of holes:	18
Length:	6516 yards (5958 metres)
Par:	71
Visitors:	Visitors welcome
Requirements:	**M**
Handicap Limits:	Gentlemen 28; Ladies 36; Juniors 28
Restrictions:	Gentlemen: not Saturdays or Wednesdays. Juniors: not Saturdays.
Parties:	Please contact Secretary/Manager well in advance.
Green fees:	£25 per day. Societies £24.
Hire facilities:	**C** **T** **Ca** **Pc**
Practice ground:	Practice ground and putting green
Catering:	Seven days per week

BRIGHT CASTLE GOLF CLUB
(ESTABLISHED 1979)
14, Coniamstown Road, Downpatrick, Co. Down, BT30 8LU

This is quite a tough and physically demanding course, with five par 5s.

Secretary:	Raymond Reid Tel 0396 841319
Professional:	None
Type:	Links
No of holes:	18
Length:	7143 yards
Par:	74
Visitors:	Visitors welcome
Requirements:	None
Handicap Limits:	Gentlemen 28; Ladies 36; Juniors 18
Restrictions:	No restrictions for Ladies, Gentlemen or Junior visitors
Parties:	Please telephone Gordon Ennis on 0396 841319 to reserve tee times
Green fees:	£10 - £12 per day. Monday to Friday after 6.00pm £7.
Hire facilities:	**T**
Practice ground:	Putting green and practice area
Catering:	Light snacks available. 'Golfers Fry' includes chips, fish, burgers etc.

CARNALEA GOLF CLUB
(ESTABLISHED 1929)
Station Road, Bangor, Co. Down, BT19 1EZ

Carnalea Golf Club is beautifully situated on the south shore of Belfast Lough about three miles west of the holiday resort of Bangor. The course occupies high ground on the rocky coastline between Stricklands Glen to the east and the clubhouse itself. It is therefore ideally placed to enjoy perfect views of Helen's Bay, Greypoint, the Antrim Hills, Scotland on a clear day and round through 180 degrees to the Copeland Islands. Carnalea is an eighteen-hole course divided into two separate nine-hole sections by the Belfast to Bangor Railway.

Secretary:	Mr J. H. Crozier Tel 0247 270368
Professional:	Shop owner: Mr J. Teggart Tel 0247 270122
Type:	Parkland
No of holes:	18
Length:	5574 yards
Par:	68
Visitors:	Visitors welcome
Requirements:	None
Handicap Limits:	None
Restrictions:	None for Gentlemen and Ladies. Visiting Juniors must be accompanied by an adult or a club member at all times.
Parties:	Parties with a minimum number of 20 are welcome except Saturday or Sunday or public holidays by arrangement with Secretary.
Green fees:	£11 per round weekdays, £15 weekends and public holidays. Juniors under 18 years £3.
Hire facilities:	C T
Practice ground:	None at present
Catering:	Full dining facilities. Contact caterer on 0247 461901.

CLANDEBOYE GOLF CLUB
(ESTABLISHED 1933)

Tower Road, Conlig, Newtownards, Co. Down, BT23 3PN

The North Down Club lies above Conlig village off the A21 between Bangor and Newtownards. The clubhouse and Dufferin course overlook the mouth of Belfast Lough, and Strangford Lough can be viewed from the Ava course. Acceptable casual dress should be worn but not denim wear. Gentlemen require jacket, collar and tie after 6.30pm in dining room.

Secretary:	Ian Marks Tel 0247 271767	
Professional:	Peter Gregory Tel 0247 271750	
	Course 1: Dufferin	**Course 2:** Ava
Type:	Parkland/Heathland	Parkland/Moorland
No of holes:	18	18
Length:	6548 yards	5755 yards
Par:	71	70

Visitors: Visitors welcome

Requirements:

Handicap Limits: None

Restrictions: All Tee times by arrangement with Secretary. Visitors can only play weekends and public holidays if playing with a member.

Parties: Contact Club Office. Parties welcome April to September on Mondays, Tuesdays, Wednesdays and Fridays; October to March on Mondays and Wednesdays.

Green fees: Dufferin £21 per round, Ava £17 per round. £30 per day. With member £10 and £9 per round.

Hire facilities:

Practice ground: Practice ground available

Catering: Full catering facilities (except on Mondays) October - March with snack, table d'hote and *à la carte* menus

Clandeboye Golf Club

THE CLIFTONVILLE GOLF CLUB LTD
(ESTABLISHED 1911)
44, Westland Road, Belfast 14

Parkland course, tree-lined. Features include winding river immediately in front of the 5th and 7th greens. Mature course with much additional tree planting taking place. Convenient location within easy reach of city centre and motorway links.

Secretary:	Mr J. Martin Henderson Tel 0232 744158/746595
Professional:	None
Type:	Parkland
No of holes:	9
Length:	2853 yards
Par:	35
Visitors:	Visitors welcome
Requirements:	None
Handicap Limits:	None
Restrictions:	No visitors on Saturday all day or Sunday mornings
Parties:	Societies welcome by prior arrangement with Secretary clubs. Requirement to complete conditions of GUI affiliated clubs and abide by their rules.
Green fees:	£10 per day weekdays. £15 weekends and public holidays. £8 or £12 when playing with members.
Hire facilities:	Ca
Practice ground:	Practice fairway, putting green and net
Catering:	Full catering available, except Mondays and Thursdays (which can be arranged with prior agreement)

DONAGHADEE GOLF CLUB
(ESTABLISHED 1899)
Warren Road, Donaghadee, Co. Down, BT21 0PQ

Part links and part inland open course. There is little rough but several
water hazards and the 18th, with out of bounds both left and right can be
problematical. Views over the Copeland Islands to the Scottish coast are
spectacular, particularly from the 16th tee.

Secretary:	Mr M. E. Dilley, Secretary/Manager
	Tel 0247 883624 Fax 0247 888891
Professional:	Tel 0247 882392
Type:	Links/parkland
No of holes:	18
Length:	5760 yards (5232 metres)
Par:	71
Visitors:	Visitors welcome
Requirements:	None
Handicap Limits:	Gentlemen 28; Ladies 36; Juniors 48
Restrictions:	No particular restrictions, but no visitors on Saturday until after 4.00pm and starting sheet operates on Sundays. Ring Professional for a time.
Parties:	Parties of 24+ Mondays, Wednesdays and Friday mornings only.
Green fees:	£14 per round, £22 per day weekdays. Sundays £18 and £28. Societies 24+ £1 off.
Hire facilities:	C T
Practice ground:	Small practice area
Catering:	Full catering facilities, except Monday

Donaghadee Golf Club: 13th hole

DOWNPATRICK GOLF CLUB LTD
(ESTABLISHED 1930)

Saul Road, Downpatrick, Co. Down, BT30 6PA

Downpatrick is a challenging parkland course situated 1½ miles from the town centre and 25 miles south of Belfast on the A7. A friendly welcome is ensured for all visitors, who will, no doubt, enjoy the superb views of miles of rolling countryside from the course.

Secretary:	Mr Joe McCoubrey Tel 0396 615947
Professional:	None
Type:	Parkland
No of holes:	18
Length:	6400 yards (5615 metres)
Par:	70
Visitors:	Visitors welcome
Requirements:	None
Handicap Limits:	None
Restrictions:	Gentlemen not between 4.30pm and 6.00pm Thursdays only; Ladies not between 3.30pm and 6.30pm Tuesdays only
Parties:	Any day by prior arrangement
Green fees:	£14 per day, weekdays, £18 per day public holidays and weekends. 20% weekday reduction for parties of 20+.
Hire facilities:	C T
Practice ground:	Putting area near first green
Catering:	Full catering service generally, but closed on Mondays. However, service would be provided if given prior notice.

DUNMURRY GOLF CLUB
(ESTABLISHED 1905)
91, Dunmurry Lane, Dunmurry, Belfast BT17 9JS

A good eighteen-hole parkland course with natural hazards.

Secretary:	Allan Taylor, Secretary/Manager
	Tel 0232 610834
Professional:	Paul Leonard Tel 0232 621314
Type:	Parkland
No of holes:	18
Length:	5348 metres
Par:	69
Visitors:	Visitors welcome
Requirements:	None
Handicap Limits:	Gentlemen 28; Ladies 36
Restrictions:	Visitors welcome by arrangement. Not available on Fridays, and on Saturdays before 5.00pm. Best availability Tuesdays to Thursdays before 5.00pm.
Parties:	Contact Secretary/Manager in writing. No Societies on Sundays.
Green fees:	£16 per round weekdays. £25 per round Sundays.
Hire facilities:	🇹
Practice ground:	Practice ground available
Catering:	No catering on Mondays

HOLYWOOD GOLF CLUB
(ESTABLISHED 1904)

Nuns Walk, Demesne Road, Holywood, Co. Down, BT18 9LE

Typical eighteen-hole parkland course.

Secretary:	David Jenkins, Secretary/Manager
	Tel 0232 423135 Fax 0232 425040
Professional:	Michael Bannon Tel 0232 425503
Type:	Parkland
No of holes:	18
Length:	5153 metres
Par:	69
Visitors:	Visitors welcome
Requirements:	None
Handicap Limits:	None
Restrictions:	No restrictions for visitors
Parties:	Contact Secretary/Manager
Green fees:	£15 per round weekdays. £20 per round Sunday:
	8.00 to 9.00am only. Groups of 20+ £13 weekdays.
Hire facilities:	C T
Practice ground:	None
Catering:	Catering and dining available. Caterer David
	Bamber 0232 426832.

KIRKISTOWN CASTLE GOLF CLUB

(ESTABLISHED 1902)

142, Main Road, Cloughey, Newtownards, Co. Down, BT22 1JA

Good semi-links course which can be affected by winds off the Irish Sea.

Secretary:	David J. Ryan Tel 02477 71233/71699
	Fax 02477 71699
Professional:	Jonathon R. Peden Tel 02477 71004
Type:	Semi-links
No of holes:	18
Length:	5596 metres
Par:	69
Visitors:	Visitors welcome
Requirements:	None
Handicap Limits:	None
Restrictions:	Restricted at competition times: Saturdays 8.00am to 1.00pm October to February, 8.00am to 2.30pm March to September. Also 9.00-10.30am and 12.00am to 1.30pm Sundays and public holidays.
Parties:	Contact Secretary/Manager. Special green fees apply - deposit required.
Green fees:	£13 per day weekdays, £25 weekends. £50 per week, £70 per fortnight, £100 for three weeks, £120 per month.
Hire facilities:	
Practice ground:	Practice fairway, bunker, green, putting and net
Catering:	Available 11.00am to 8.00pm Monday to Saturday, 12.00am to 6.00pm Sunday. Caterer Marion Smyth 02477 71353

KNOCK GOLF CLUB

(ESTABLISHED 1895)

Summerfield, Dundonald, Belfast, BT16 0QX

Two eighteen-hole parkland courses.

Secretary:	Mr S. G. Managh Tel 0232 483251
Professional:	Gordon Fairweather Tel 0232 483825
Type:	Parkland
No of holes:	18
Length:	6435 yards
Par:	70
Visitors:	Visitors welcome
Requirements:	None
Handicap Limits:	Gentlemen 28; Ladies 36; Juniors 28
Restrictions:	Tee reserved for members; Ladies 9.00 - 10.00am every day and 1.00-2.00pm Tuesday, Wednesday, Friday, Saturday and Sunday. Also Tuesday and Friday 4.30 - 6.00pm.
Parties:	Please contact Secretary
Green fees:	£20 per day weekdays, £24 weekends. Societies £16.
Hire facilities:	C T
Practice ground:	Limited facilities. Net available.
Catering:	Available every day

MALONE GOLF CLUB
(ESTABLISHED 1895)
240 Upper Malone Road, Dunmurry, Belfast, BT17 9LB

Set in attractive parkland, the centrepiece is a beautiful lake some 25 acres in extent. This is stocked with trout and other sporting fish and comes very much into play on the back nine, which are reckoned to be more difficult than the front nine. Some of the holes have been compared with Augusta, where the greens are placed near the water's edge. Trees are also a feature and the setting is of great beauty.

The clubhouse dates from about 1835 and strict jacket-and-tie rules apply. Malone is situated four miles south of Belfast city.

Secretary:	Mr T. H. Young, Secretary/Manager Tel 01232 612758
Professional:	Mr M. McGee Tel 01232 431394
Type:	Parkland
No of holes:	18
Length:	6476 yards
Par:	71
Visitors:	Visitors welcome
Requirements:	M
Handicap Limits:	None
Restrictions:	All visitors restricted Wednesdays and Saturdays. Time sheets operate on Saturdays and Sundays.
Parties:	Please contact Secretary/Manager. Monday and Thursday only.
Green fees:	Currently £30 per round. No special rates.
Hire facilities:	C T Ca Pc B
Practice ground:	Practice facilities for members only
Catering:	Catering by arrangement

MOUNT OBER GOLF & COUNTRY CLUB (KNOCKBRACKEN)

(ESTABLISHED 1985)

24 Ballymaconaghy Road, Knockbracken, Belfast, BT8 4SB

Club name recently changed from Knockbracken Golf Club to Mount Ober Golf & Country Club. Eighteen-hole undulating parkland course, the centrepiece of a multi-sports complex.

Secretary:	Malcolm Grose Tel 0232 795666
Professional:	David Jones, Geoff Loughrey, Chris Spence (PGA) Tel 0232 792108
Type:	Parkland
No of holes:	18
Length:	5391 yards
Par:	67
Visitors:	Visitors welcome
Requirements:	None
Handicap Limits:	None
Restrictions:	All visitors restricted Saturday after 3.30pm and Sunday after 10.30am
Parties:	Please contact Margaret Jefferson, Secretary's office
Green fees:	£10 per round weekdays, £12 weekends (£9 and £10 with member)
Hire facilities:	C T Pc
Practice ground:	Putting green and small practice ground
Catering:	Catering facilities available in clubhouse and Ski Lodge

ROYAL BELFAST GOLF CLUB
(ESTABLISHED 1881)
Craigavad, Holywood, Co. Down

Originally established at the Kinnegar, Holywood, the club moved to a site in Carnalea at Bangor, but when that proved inadequate the final move was made in 1925 when Craigavad House and Demesne became available. This has now become established as one of the finest eighteen-hole parkland settings in the game. Local knowledge has it that all putts tend to fall towards the sea, and it is generally accepted that accuracy rather than length is the prime requirement for this course, which was laid out by H. S. Colt, the well-known architect of the day.

Secretary:	Ian M. Piggot Tel 0232 428165
Professional:	David Carson Tel 0232 428586
Type:	Parkland and loughside
No of holes:	18
Length:	5963 yards
Par:	70
Visitors:	Visitors welcome by prior arrangement
Requirements:	H M
Handicap Limits:	None
Restrictions:	Juniors with members only. Gentlemen and Ladies not allowed on Wednesday and Thursday afternoons or on Saturdays before 4.30pm.
Parties:	Please contact the Secretary
Green fees:	(1994) £25 per round weekday, £30 weekends and public holidays
Hire facilities:	C T Pc
Practice ground:	Practice fairway and green
Catering:	Full catering facilities

Royal Belfast Golf Club

Royal County Down Golf Club

ROYAL COUNTY DOWN GOLF CLUB
(ESTABLISHED 1889)
Newcastle, Co. Down, BT33 OAN

A beautiful course, set against the background of the Mountains of Mourne and moulded into the existing terrain with the minimum of adjustment. The course has five tee shots which are blind and for a number of approach shots the greens are partially obscured. The course is kept in excellent condition and the greens are fast and difficult to read. An exceptional test of golfing skill. A second course of par 65 is also available.

Secretary:	Mr P. E. Rolph Tel 03967 23314
	Fax 03967 26281
Professional:	Mr K. J. Whitson Tel 03967 22419

	Course 1: Championship Course	**Course 2:** No. 2
Type:	Links	Links
No of holes:	18	18
Length:	6969 yards	4087 yards
Par:	71	65

Visitors:	Visitors welcome
Requirements:	**H**
Handicap Limits:	Gentlemen 28; Ladies 36; Juniors 28
Restrictions:	All visitors should avoid weekends and Wednesdays
Parties:	Please contact Secretary
Green fees:	Championship course £43 per round, £53 per day weekdays; £55 and £65 weekends. No. 2 course £8 and £12.

Hire facilities:	**C** **T** **Ca** **Pc**
Practice ground:	Practice ground available
Catering:	Centenary Room: bar and catering. Casual dress weekdays only.

SCRABO GOLF CLUB
(ESTABLISHED 1907)
233, Scrabo Road, Newtownards, Co. Down, BT23 4SL

A scenic course approximately ten miles from Belfast off the main Belfast/ Newtownards dual carriageway and two miles west of Newtownards by Scrabo Tower. Highly recommended full catering facilities (Mondays excepted).

Secretary:	James Fraser, Secretary/Manager Tel 0247 812355 Fax 0247 822919
Professional:	Gordon Fairweather Tel 0247 817848
Type:	Upland
No of holes:	18
Length:	6235 yards (5699 metres)
Par:	71
Visitors:	Visitors welcome
Requirements:	H
Handicap Limits:	Gentlemen 28; Ladies 36
Restrictions:	Gentlemen Wednesday 4.30 to 6.30pm; Ladies Saturday before 4.30pm; Juniors Monday to Friday after 5.00pm. Saturday and Sunday before 5.00pm.
Parties:	Please contact Secretary/Manager
Green fees:	£15 per round. Special rates for societies.
Hire facilities:	C T Ca
Practice ground:	Available close to clubhouse
Catering:	Catering facilities available every day except Monday

SHANDON PARK GOLF CLUB
(ESTABLISHED 1926)
73, Shandon Park, Belfast, BT5 6NY

A very interesting, highly rated eighteen-hole parkland course.

Secretary:	Michael Corsar, General Manager
	Tel 0232 401856
Professional:	Barry Wilson Tel 0232 797859
Type:	Parkland
No of holes:	18
Length:	6252 yards
Par:	70
Visitors:	Visitors welcome
Requirements:	None
Handicap Limits:	None
Restrictions:	Gentlemen: no restriction except Saturdays when no visitors. Ladies and Juniors may play all day Tuesday and Thursday.
Parties:	Societies welcome May to October only on Monday and Friday
Green fees:	£20 per round
Hire facilities:	🇨 🇹
Practice ground:	Practice ground available
Catering:	Full catering facilities

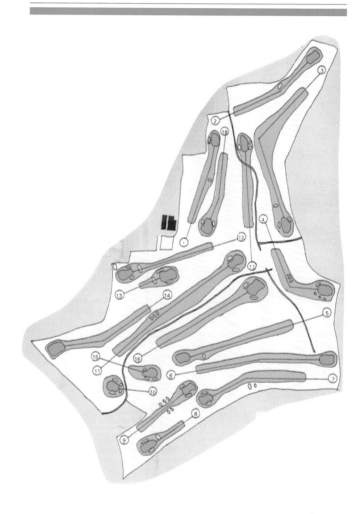

Shandon Park Golf Club: course plan

SPA GOLF CLUB
(ESTABLISHED 1907)
20, Grove Road, Ballynahinch, Co. Down, BT24 8PN

A tricky eighteen-hole parkland course with some very fine scenic mountain views.

Secretary:	Mr J. McGlass Tel 0238 562365
Professional:	None
Type:	18
No of holes:	18
Length:	5938 metres
Par:	72
Visitors:	Visitors welcome
Requirements:	None
Handicap Limits:	None
Restrictions:	Visitors welcome Monday to Thurdays inclusive, 8.30am to 6.00pm. Juniors must be accompanied by an adult.
Parties:	Mondays, Tuesdays and Thursdays only. Contact Hon. Secretary.
Green fees:	£12.50 per round, £16.50 public holidays. For daily rates apply to Hon. Secretary.
Hire facilities:	None
Practice ground:	Practice ground and nets available
Catering:	Catering facilities available

WARRENPOINT GOLF CLUB
(ESTABLISHED 1893)
Lower Dromore Road, Warrenpoint, Co. Down

The home club of Ronan Rafferty. A lovely eighteen-hole parkland course with fine scenery and many mature trees.

Secretary:	John McMahon Tel 06937 53695
	Fax 06937 52918
Professional:	Nigel Shaw Tel 06937 52371
Type:	Parkland
No of holes:	18
Length:	6100 yards
Par:	71
Visitors:	Visitors welcome
Requirements:	H M
Handicap Limits:	Gentlemen 28; Ladies 36; Juniors 28
Restrictions:	All tee times to be arranged with Secretary
Parties:	Please arrange with Secretary
Green fees:	£16 per round
Hire facilities:	C T Ca (by prior arrangement) Pc B
Practice ground:	None
Catering:	Restaurant/bar facilities available

ENNISKILLEN GOLF CLUB
(ESTABLISHED 1896)
Castlecoole, Enniskillen, Co. Fermanagh, BT74 6HZ

This is a very picturesque parkland course with many magnificent mature trees - oak, beech, chestnut. Panoramic views for first nine holes. Excellent holiday/society golf with a very warm welcome in an unpretentious clubhouse.

Secretary:	Mr W. J. Hamilton Tel 0365 25250
Professional:	None
Type:	Parkland
No of holes:	18
Length:	6147 yards (5588 metres)
Par:	71
Visitors:	Visitors welcome
Requirements:	None
Handicap Limits:	Gentlemen 28; Ladies 36; Juniors 28
Restrictions:	No restrictions for visitors
Parties:	Please contact Club Steward
Green fees:	£12 per round. Reductions for Societies of 12 or more
Hire facilities:	C T
Practice ground:	None
Catering:	Catering facilities available by request

CASTLEROCK GOLF CLUB
(ESTABLISHED 1901)
65, Circular Road, Castlerock, Co. Londonderry

To get to Castlerock, follow the coast road from Portrush west of the town for nine miles. The course seems to have been overshadowed by Royal Portrush and the neighbouring Portstewart, but why it's not more renowned defies logic. It has a combination of beauty, challenge and sheer fun that are magnetic. Set in undulating and elevated duneland at the mouth of the River Bann, the scenery is spectacular and views from the 17th tee alone are worth any detour. Laid out by Ben Sayers in 1901, the course zigzags between the soaring dunes. A memorable golfing experience.

Secretary:	Mr R. G. McBride, Secretary/Manager Tel 0265 848314	
Professional:	Mr R. Kelly Tel 0265 848314	
	Course 1: Mussenden	**Course 2:** Bann
Type:	Links	Links
No of holes:	18	9
Length:	6687 yards	2457 metres
Par:	73	35

Visitors:	Visitors welcome
Requirements:	[M]
Handicap Limits:	None
Restrictions:	All visitors restricted Friday, Saturday and Sunday.
Parties:	Please contact Secretary/Manager
Green fees:	£15 per round, £25 per day weekdays. Weekends and public holidays £25 per round.
Hire facilities:	[C] [T] [Ca]
Practice ground:	Comprehensive practice area
Catering:	Full snack and dining room facilities

CITY OF DERRY GOLF CLUB
(ESTABLISHED 1912)
49 Victoria Road, Prehen, Londonderry, BT47 2PU

Over the years the course has been extended on a number of occasions to the present twenty-seven-hole complex which includes an eighteen-hole championship course and a challenging nine-hole hillside course. The championship course has outstanding variety, with lush green fairways meandering through mature woodland and clumps of gorse to trap the careless tee shot. With impressive views of the River Foyle, this challenging course enjoys one of the most picturesque settings anywhere in the world.

Secretary:	Colum B. Murphy Tel 0504 46369	
Professional:	Michael Doherty Tel 0504 311496	
	Course 1: Prehen	**Course 2:** Dunhugh
Type:	Parkland	Parkland
No of holes:	18	9
Length:	6487 yards	2354 yards
Par:	71	33

Visitors: Visitors welcome

Requirements: Ⓗ

Handicap Limits: Gentlemen 28; Ladies 36; Juniors 28

Restrictions: All visitors to telephone to reserve tee times. Juniors restricted 8.00am to 4.00pm.

Parties: Contact May Kirby on 0504 46369. Reductions for parties over 20.

Green fees: £11 per round weekdays. £13 weekends and public holidays. Special rates negotiable.

Hire facilities: Ⓣ   Ⓑ

Practice ground: Available to members only

Catering: Available weekly and weekends. Societies by prior arrangement.

MOYOLA PARK GOLF CLUB

Shanemullagh, Curran Road, Castledawson, Magherafelt,
Co. Londonderry

The course is located in a mature parkland setting on the estate of Lord Moyola. A challenging test for golfers of all levels. The signature hole is the 423 yard 8th, requiring a long, well-placed tee shot to set up a testing approach through a tree-lined corridor over the Moyola River.

Secretary:	Mr L. W. P. Hastings, Hon. Sec. Tel 0648 32796/31271
Professional:	Mr V. Teague Tel 0648 68830
Type:	Parkland
No of holes:	18
Length:	6522 yards
Par:	71
Visitors:	Visitors welcome
Requirements:	None
Handicap Limits:	None
Restrictions:	Gentlemen restricted Wednesday before 5.30pm, Saturday and Sunday. Ladies Saturday and Sunday, and Juniors Monday to Friday after 4.30pm and Saturday and Sunday.
Parties:	Please contact Mr. P. W. Hastings and prebook
Green fees:	£12 per day Monday to Friday, £22 Sunday. No special rates.
Hire facilities:	C T Ca
Practice ground:	Practice ground and putting green
Catering:	Catering available. Contact Caterer, John Crosskerry on 0648 68392.

PORTSTEWART GOLF CLUB
(ESTABLISHED 1894)
117, Strand Road, Portstewart, Co. Londonderry

When the club was founded in 1894 it had a short nine-hole course at the start of the present day 'Old Course'. In 1908 the headquarters were transferred to the Strand Course, which was laid out by Mr Gow of Portrush, and this remained largely unchanged until further land purchase in the 1960s permitted more expansion. This was of a dual character, the first nine holes skirting the sand dunes to provide classic links ground while the second nine has more of an inland character. In 1992 a further extension into the dune made a second nine-hole course - 'The Riverside'.

Secretary:	Michael Moss, Manager Tel 026583 2015 Fax 026583 4097	
Professional:	Alan Hunter Tel 026583 2601	

	Course 1: Strand	**Course 2:** Riverside
Type:	Links/inland	Links/inland
No of holes:	18	9
Length:	6784 yards	2662 yards
Par:	72	32

	Course 3: Old
Type:	Links/inland
No of holes:	18
Length:	4733 yards
Par:	64

Visitors:	Visitors welcome
Requirements:	H for Strand course only
Handicap Limits:	Gentlemen 28; Ladies 36; Juniors 36
Restrictions:	All visitors restricted Strand Course Saturday and Sunday, but accepted Monday to Friday by arrangement. All categories welcome at Riverside and Old Courses, but prior booking desirable.
Parties:	Please contact Manager's Office

Green fees:	Strand £25 per round, £35 per day. Riverside £10 and £20. Old £10 per round. Reductions for groups over 16.
Hire facilities:	C T Ca Pc
Practice ground:	Excellent practice facilities
Catering:	Catering available - extensive menu

Portstewart Golf Club: 2nd hole

Portstewart Golf Club: 18th hole

DUNGANNON GOLF CLUB
(ESTABLISHED 1890)
34 Springfield Lane, Dungannon, Co. Tyrone

A rolling parkland course with flat first nine and hilly second nine holes with mainly wide fairways. Very accessible, being close to the 'North-west Passage' from Newry to Londonderry, close to the western limit of the M1 motorway. Uncluttered weekdays, but note restricted hours/tee availability Tuesdays (Ladies Day). Always ring before you come.

Secretary:	Mr L. R. P. Agnew, Hon Secretary
	Tel 0868 727338 Fax 0868 722098
Professional:	None
Type:	Parkland
No of holes:	18
Length:	5433 metres
Par:	71
Visitors:	Visitors welcome
Requirements:	None
Handicap Limits:	None
Restrictions:	Gentlemen restricted: time sheets Tuesday, Saturday and Sunday. Ladies time sheets: Saturday, Sunday, Thursday; Juniors: no play after 4.30pm weekdays.
Parties:	Please contact Office (Secretary)
Green fees:	£10 per day weekday, £13 weekends. £2 discount if playing with a member.
Hire facilities:	**T**
Practice ground:	Putting green
Catering:	Franchised catering by appointment

KILLYMOON GOLF CLUB
(ESTABLISHED 1889)
200 Killymoon Road, Cookstown, Co. Tyrone, BT80 8TW

Situated on the outskirts of Cookstown, the club is named after Killymoon Castle, designed in 1804 by John Nash and reputedly owned at one time by King George IV, who is said to have won it on the throw of a dice. The course is parkland, reasonably flat and quite challenging. In 1891 an unknown author wrote of the then nine-hole course: "The dreary sand associated with conventional Scotch links is absent from Killymoon but only to be replaced by firm old sward and the tiresome sameness of the dunes exchanged for the most diversified views of wooded hills and valleys".

Secretary:	Mr L. Hodgett Tel 06487 63762
Professional:	Mr P. A. Coint Tel 06487 63460
Type:	Parkland
No of holes:	18
Length:	6013 yards
Par:	70
Visitors:	Visitors welcome by appointment
Requirements:	**H** **M**
Handicap Limits:	None
Restrictions:	Visitors must make prior arrangements
Parties:	By arrangement with Secretary
Green fees:	£14 per round weekdays, £18 weekends
Hire facilities:	Details not supplied
Practice ground:	Practice ground available
Catering:	Catering facilities available

OMAGH GOLF CLUB
(ESTABLISHED 1910)
83a Dublin Road, Omagh, Co. Tyrone BT78 1HQ

Parkland courses with fine scenery.

Secretary:	Mrs Florence E. A. Caldwell. (Mr J. A. McElholm Hon. Secretary) Tel 0662 243160/241442
Professional:	None

	Course 1: White	**Course 2:** Green
Type:	Parkland	Parkland
No of holes:	18	18
Length:	5636 metres	5429 metres
Par:	71	72

Visitors:	Visitors welcome
Requirements:	None
Handicap Limits:	None
Restrictions:	Gentlemen restricted Tuesdays - Ladies Day. Ladies restricted weekends during mens' competitions. Juniors (with adult) after 4.30pm.
Parties:	Contact Secretary
Green fees:	£10 per day weekdays. £15 weekends. £2 reduction with member. OAPs, Students, Juniors: half fee weekdays.
Hire facilities:	None
Practice ground:	None
Catering:	Contact Secretary: bar facilities available

STRABANE GOLF CLUB
(ESTABLISHED 1908)
Ballycolman, Strabane, Co. Tyrone

Parkland course with lovely views - particularly the 4th and 15th holes.

Secretary:	Terry Doherty Tel 0504 382007
Professional:	None
Type:	Parkland
No of holes:	18
Length:	5552 metres
Par:	68
Visitors:	Visitors welcome
Requirements:	M
Handicap Limits:	Gentlemen 28; Ladies 38; Juniors 12
Restrictions:	All visitors tee times must be pre-arranged
Parties:	Contact Terry Doherty or Collette Kelly on 0504 382007
Green fees:	£10 per day. (£8 with member)
Hire facilities:	Ca
Practice ground:	No practice ground
Catering:	Catering facilities available by arrangement

ULSTER (REPUBLIC) GOLF CLUBS

Co. Cavan
County Cavan
Slieve Russell

Co. Donegal
Ballybofey &
  Stranorlar
Ballyliffin

Bundoran
Donegal
Dunfanaghy
Gweedore
Letterkenny
Narin & Portnoo
North-West
Portsalon
Rosapenna

Co. Monagan
Nuremore
Rossmore

COUNTY CAVAN GOLF CLUB
(ESTABLISHED 1894)
Arnmore House, Drumellis, Co. Cavan

In 1994 County Cavan Golf Club celebrated 100 years of golf. It is a typical parkland course and a true test of golf. The par 3s are a feature and if you can include four threes in your round you are indeed playing well.

Secretary:	Tommy Sheridan Tel 049 32183
Professional:	None
Type:	Parkland
No of holes:	18
Length:	5942 yards (5521 metres)
Par:	70
Visitors:	Visitors welcome
Requirements:	None
Handicap Limits:	None
Restrictions:	Ladies and Juniors restricted on days of men's competitions
Parties:	Contact Secretary. Some weekend dates available in the morning.
Green fees:	IR£10 per day weekdays, IR£12 weekends
Hire facilities:	**B**
Practice ground:	Full length practice ground
Catering:	Full catering facilities available on request

SLIEVE RUSSELL GOLF CLUB
(ESTABLISHED 1992)
Ballyconnell, Co. Cavan

This championship standard gold course and practice facility stretches over a 300-acre estate including 50 acres of lakes and ponds. Its unique style fits and complements the typical Cavan drumlin and valley landscape, with gently tumbling fairways and contoured greens. The clubhouse overlooking the course incorporates the Summit Bar and Restaurant. Facilities also include a golf shop and club storage area. A nine-hole par 3 course was due to open in 1994.

Secretary:	Packie McKiernan Tel 049 26444	
Professional:	Liam McCool Tel 049 26444	

	Course 1: Slieve Russell	**Course 2:**
Type:	Parkland	Parkland
No of holes:	18	9
Length:	Medal 6580 yards (6018 metres)	To be confirmed
Par:	72	27

Visitors: Visitors welcome
Requirements: ⬛ H   ⬛ M
Handicap Limits: None
Restrictions: No restrictions but must pre-book. Special rates for groups of 20 or more playing in four balls. Details available on request.
Parties: Please contact Shirley Sweeney on 049 26444
Green fees: IR£22 Sunday to Friday per round, IR£30 Saturday. Four balls IR£80 per round Sunday to Friday, IR£110 Saturday.

Hire facilities: ⬛ C   ⬛ T   ⬛ Ca   ⬛ Pc   ⬛ B
Practice ground: Practice putting green and practice area
Catering: 90-seater restaurant in clubhouse, with bar, attached to Slieve Russell Hotel

Score card details

Hole	1	2	3	4	5	6	7	8	9	10	11	12	13	14	15	16	17	18
Yds	389	407	371	159	412	491	196	338	509	393	168	434	502	356	426	165	345	519
Par	4	4	4	3	4	5	3	4	5	4	3	5	5	4	4	3	4	5

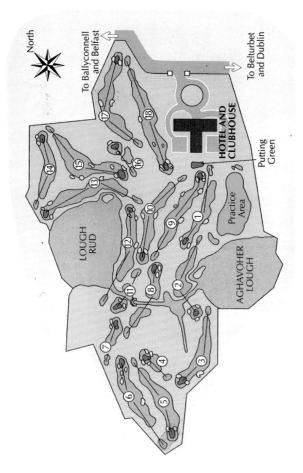

Slieve Russell Golf Club: course plan

BALLYBOFEY AND STRANORLAR GOLF CLUB
(ESTABLISHED 1958)
Ballybofey, Co. Donegal

A parkland course with views of Finn valley - three holes alongside Lough Alan. A quarter of a mile from Stranorlar - good hotels available: Kee's Hotel in Stranorlar and Jackson's Hotel in Ballybofey. The course has very fine par 3 holes and is in best condition from May to September/October.

Secretary:	Patrick Carr Tel 074 31104
Professional:	None Club tel: 074 31093
Type:	Parkland
No of holes:	18
Length:	5905 yards (5366 metres)
Par:	68
Visitors:	Visitors welcome
Requirements:	None
Handicap Limits:	Gentlemen 28; Ladies 36
Restrictions:	All visitors up to 3.00pm Monday and Tuesday, up to 6.00pm Wednesday, Thursday and Friday. Bookings required Saturday and Sunday, subject to local competitions.
Parties:	Please telephone J. McGettigan on 074 31033
Green fees:	IR£12 per round. Reduction for groups.
Hire facilities:	None
Practice ground:	Practice area available
Catering:	Catering franchise in operation: snacks at all times and full meals by arrangement with Steward

BALLYLIFFIN GOLF CLUB
(ESTABLISHED 1947)
Ballyliffin, Carndonagh, Co. Donegal

Ballyliffin Golf Club was founded in 1947 and moved to its present
location in 1970. It has a new clubhouse built in 1987, and a second
eighteen holes (designed by Craddock and Ruddy) were started in 1993
and are due to open summer 1995, when a new clubhouse is also to start
construction. Nick Faldo visited in June 1993 and later described
Ballyliffin as the 'Royal Dornoch' of Ireland. Fred Daly described
Ballyliffin as 'a hidden jewel'. It is Ireland's most northerly course.

Secretary:	Karl J. O'Doherty Tel 077 76119/74417
Professional:	None
Type:	Seaside links
No of holes:	18
Length:	6384 yards
Par:	72
Visitors:	Visitors welcome
Requirements:	M
Handicap Limits:	None
Restrictions:	Weekends: Ladies not before 2.00pm
Parties:	Please contact Karl O'Doherty. Special rates for parties of over 10.
Green fees:	IR£12 per day weekdays, IR£15 weekends
Hire facilities:	T Ca
Practice ground:	Full practice area available
Catering:	Catering facilities available by arrangement for large parties

BUNDORAN GOLF CLUB
(ESTABLISHED 1894)
Great Northern Hotel, Bundoran, Co. Donegal

The course was designed by the great Harry Vardon and was an early training ground for the illustrious Christy O'Connor. Bundoran is a challenging par 69 of 6159 yards. It sweeps along the sea with a mix of dunes and undulating terrain.

Secretary:	Mr L. McDevitt Tel 072 41302
Professional:	Mr D. T. Robinson Tel 072 41302
Type:	Links
No of holes:	18
Length:	6159 yards
Par:	69
Visitors:	Visitors welcome
Requirements:	None
Handicap Limits:	Gentlemen 28; Ladies 36; Juniors 28
Restrictions:	No restrictions
Parties:	Please contact Professional, D. Robinson
Green fees:	IR£12 per round, IR£14 weekends. IR£20 per day.
Hire facilities:	C T Ca
Practice ground:	Practice ground available
Catering:	Snacks in clubhouse. Hotel attached to course.

DONEGAL GOLF CLUB
(ESTABLISHED 1960)
Murvagh, Laghey, Co. Donegal

Donegal Golf Links is situated on the beautiful Murvagh in Donegal Bay. It is screened from the outside world by a forest of evergreens with the Bluestack Mountains in the background. Recently used by Nick Faldo in his preparation for his third victory in the Irish Open, Murvagh, as it is popularly known, is one of the longest links in the British Isles and is always featured in any ratings published.

Secretary:	Jim Nixon Tel 073 34054 Fax 073 34377
Professional:	None
Type:	Links
No of holes:	18
Length:	6863 yards (6243 metres)
Par:	73
Visitors:	Visitors welcome
Requirements:	H M
Handicap Limits:	Gentlemen 28; Ladies 36; Juniors 12
Restrictions:	Gentlemen and Juniors restricted Sundays and Mondays. Ladies restricted Sundays but limited times available on Mondays (Ladies Day).
Parties:	Contact John McBride (Administrator) 073 34054
Green fees:	IR£15 per round weekdays, IR£18 Saturday, Sunday and public holidays. Special rates for societies.
Hire facilities:	C T B
Practice ground:	Large practice ground
Catering:	Catering every day

Score card details

Hole	1	2	3	4	5	6	7	8	9	10	11	12	13	14	15	16	17	18
Mtre	478	379	173	380	170	473	352	499	306	320	340	503	145	479	370	209	323	344
Par	5	4	3	4	3	5	4	5	4	4	4	5	3	5	4	3	4	4

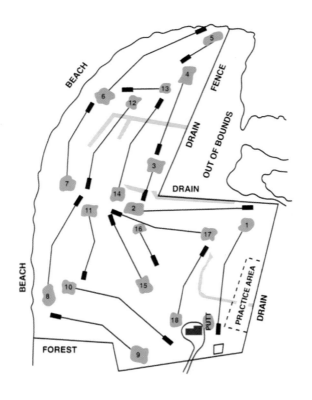

Donegal Golf Club: course plan

Donegal Golf Club: views

DUNFANAGHY GOLF CLUB

(ESTABLISHED 1906)

Dunfanaghy, Co. Donegal

The course is set between Port-na-Blagh and Horn Head on the coast road overlooking Sheephaven Bay. Flat central area comprising the 1st, 2nd, 3rd, 4th, 5th, 11th, 12th, 13th with three difficult streams to negotiate. At the Port-na-Blagh end, five marvellous holes featuring a 205 metre par 3 (7th) from the most elevated point to a difficult sloping green, a short par 3 (9th) across the beach to a two-tier green, and a treacherous 10th from an elevated tee, with a dogleg right and the out of bounds beach on the right. At the Horn Head end the last five holes are a test for any golfer.

Secretary:	Mary Doherty Tel 074 36335
Professional:	None
Type:	Links
No of holes:	18
Length:	5006 metres
Par:	68
Visitors:	Visitors welcome
Requirements:	None
Handicap Limits:	None
Restrictions:	Gentlemen and Ladies restricted Saturdays 9.30 to 10.30 and 11.00 to 12.00am, Sundays 9.30 to 10.30am and 12.00 to 2.00pm. Juniors not before 6.00pm any day.
Parties:	Please contact Mary Doherty on 074 36335
Green fees:	IR£11 weekdays, IR£13 weekends. IR£7 with member.
Hire facilities:	[C] [T]
Practice ground:	Practice net and putting green
Catering:	Bar snacks: soup, tea, sandwiches

GWEEDORE GOLF CLUB
(ESTABLISHED 1926)
Magheragallen, Derrybeg, Letterkenny, Co. Donegal

Links course situated in Gweedore, in the heart of the Donegal Gaeltacht at the north-west point of the Irish coast. Magnificent sea and mountain views. Unrestricted play: visitors most welcome. Stampeding sheep may appear without notice!

Secretary:	E. McBride Tel 075 31666
Professional:	None
Type:	Links
No of holes:	9 (played from outward and inward tees)
Length:	6201 yards
Par:	71
Visitors:	Visitors welcome
Requirements:	None
Handicap Limits:	None
Restrictions:	No restrictions for visitors
Parties:	Please contact Secretary
Green fees:	IR£7 per day. Special rates for societies and groups.
Hire facilities:	None
Practice ground:	Practice area adjacent to course
Catering:	Catering available during holiday season, June to September.

LETTERKENNY GOLF CLUB
(ESTABLISHED 1913)

Barnhill, Letterkenny, Co. Donegal

Letterkenny is an eighteen-hole parkland course situated about two miles from Letterkenny. It is convenient to local hotels and guest houses. The main feature of the course is an abundance of trees which play a main part in the course design. The first tee is elevated and gives a very picturesque view of Lough Swilly. The first half of the course is basically flat and the second half undulating and hilly.

Secretary:	Charles McHugh Tel 074 21150
Professional:	None
Type:	Parkland
No of holes:	18
Length:	6239 yards
Par:	70
Visitors:	Visitors welcome
Requirements:	None
Handicap Limits:	Gentlemen 28; Ladies 36
Restrictions:	Visitors welcome weekdays but must request time at weekends. Juniors may play Monday to Friday but not after 6.00pm.
Parties:	Please contact Secretary
Green fees:	IR£10 per round
Hire facilities:	C T
Practice ground:	Practice ground and practice green
Catering:	Catering facilities available

NARIN AND PORTNOO GOLF CLUB
(ESTABLISHED 1930)
Narin, Portnoo, Co. Donegal

The course is quite short but very tight. Accuracy is the order of the day and because of the situation on the Atlantic coast the wind plays a big part in any round. Narin and Portnoo Golf Club is one of the most picturesque courses in the country with breathtaking views from many of the tees.

Secretary:	Tony Boner Tel 073 39221
Professional:	None
Type:	Links
No of holes:	18
Length:	5322 metres
Par:	69
Visitors:	Visitors welcome
Requirements:	None
Handicap Limits:	Gentlemen 28; Ladies 36; Juniors 28
Restrictions:	Gentlemen restricted Saturday and Sunday 1.00 - 2.30pm. Ladies Day Tuesday. Ladies restricted Sundays until time sheet complete.
Parties:	Contact Sean Murphy, Club Manager. No societies during July and August.
Green fees:	IR£10 per round weekdays, IR£13 at weekends. No special rates.
Hire facilities:	None
Practice ground:	Putting green
Catering:	Hot meals available in clubhouse

NORTH-WEST GOLF CLUB
(ESTABLISHED 1892)
Lisfannon, Fahan, Co. Donegal

A testing links course.

Secretary:	Sean Doherty Tel 077 61715
Professional:	Seamus McBriarty Tel 077 61715
Type:	Links
No of holes:	18
Length:	5968 yards
Par:	69
Visitors:	Visitors welcome
Requirements:	H M
Handicap Limits:	Gentlemen 28; Ladies 36; Juniors 15
Restrictions:	All visitors restricted only on Saturdays and Sundays
Parties:	Please contact Professional (077 61725)
Green fees:	IR£10 per round or per day. No special rates.
Hire facilities:	T Ca
Practice ground:	Small practice area
Catering:	Catering/dining facilities provided

PORTSALON GOLF CLUB
(ESTABLISHED 1891)
Portsalon, Fanad, Letterkenny, Co. Donegal

A typical links course layout.

Secretary:	Cathal Toland Tel 074 59459
Professional:	None
Type:	Links
No of holes:	18
Length:	5878 yards
Par:	69
Visitors:	Visitors welcome
Requirements:	None
Handicap Limits:	None
Restrictions:	No restrictions
Parties:	Please contact Secretary
Green fees:	IR£10 per day (IR£12 weekends). IR£6 with full member, IR£8 with country member.
Hire facilities:	T
Practice ground:	No practice ground
Catering:	Catering facilities available

ROSAPENNA GOLF CLUB
(ESTABLISHED 1895)
Rosapenna, Downings, Co. Donegal

The course is owned by a hotel, which looks after all the golfing facilities. The hotel manager has complete control of the course and the members run the club. A new nine-hole course is under construction which is being scheduled to open during the club centenary year, 1995. The Rospenna Golf Hotel is situated one mile from Downings.

Secretary:	Michael J. Gallagher Tel 074 55264
Professional:	None
Type:	Inland links
No of holes:	18
Length:	6271 yards
Par:	70
Visitors:	Visitors welcome
Requirements:	None
Handicap Limits:	None
Restrictions:	None stated - tee times available on request to Secretary.
Parties:	Please contact Rosapenna Hotel on 074 55301, Proprietor Frank Casey
Green fees:	IR£15 per day midweek, IR£20 weekends. Special rates for parties on request.
Hire facilities:	T Ca
Practice ground:	Putting green and practice area for mid-irons
Catering:	Grill bar in the hotel

NUREMORE HOTEL AND COUNTRY CLUB
(ESTABLISHED 1964)
Carrickmacross, Co. Monaghan

A good holiday course featuring a lake on the 8th.

Secretary:	Sean Egan Tel 042 62125
Professional:	Maurice Cassidy Tel 042 61438
	Fax 042 61853
Type:	Parkland
No of holes:	18
Length:	5900 metres
Par:	72
Visitors:	Visitors welcome
Requirements:	None
Handicap Limits:	None
Restrictions:	No restrictions for gentlemen or ladies. Juniors restricted only at weekends.
Parties:	Please contact Maurice Cassidy or Helen Woods
Green fees:	IR£15 per day midweek, IR£18 weekends
Hire facilities:	C T Ca
Practice ground:	Practice area, but not adjacent to first tee
Catering:	Catering facilities available in both hotel and golf pavilion

ROSSMORE PARK GOLF CLUB
(ESTABLISHED 1916)
Rossmore Park, Monaghan, Co. Monaghan

Eighteen-hole parkland layout with water.

Secretary:	Jimmie McKenna Tel 046 81316
Professional:	None
Type:	Parkland
No of holes:	18
Length:	5605 metres
Par:	70
Visitors:	Visitors welcome
Requirements:	None
Handicap Limits:	Gentlemen 28; Ladies 36; Juniors 36
Restrictions:	Restrictions only on days of club competitions
Parties:	Please contact Jimmie McKenna. Deposit required.
Green fees:	IR£10 per day. Societies IR£8.
Hire facilities:	None
Practice ground:	None
Catering:	Full catering available between 12 noon and 9.30pm Tuesday to Sunday

INDEX OF GOLF CLUBS

ACKNOWLEDGEMENTS

The publishers would like to thank the following for permission to publish their photographs:

Westport Golf Club: Bord Fáilte Photograph (Pat Odea)
Portmarnock Golf Club, Royal Dublin Golf Club, County Louth Golf Club (bottom), Mullingar Golf Club, Rosslare Golf Club, Ballybunion Golf Club: Bord Fáilte photograph (Brian Lynch)
Killarney Golf & Fishing Club: Phil Inglis
Ballycastle Golf Club, Lisburn Golf Club, Royal Portrush Golf Club, Clandeboye Golf Club and Royal Belfast Golf Club: Northern Ireland Tourist Board

All other photographs are supplied by the respective clubs.

The publishers would also like to express their thanks to Simon Tormey of Bord Fáilte for all his help, patience and advice.